ENRICHMENT MASTERS

Algebra 1

HOLT, RINEHART AND WINSTON

A Harcourt Classroom Education Company

Austin • New York • Orlando • Atlanta • San Francisco • Boston • Dallas • Toronto • London

To the Teacher

Algebra 1 Enrichment Masters contain one-page blackline masters for each of the 87 lessons in *Algebra 1*. These masters provide stimulating problems, projects, games, and puzzles that extend and/or enrich the lesson material.

Photo Credit
Front Cover: (background), Index Stock Photography Inc./Ron Russell; (bottom), Jean Miele MCMXCII/The Stock Market.

Printed in the United States of America

ISBN 0-03-054283-9

5   6   7   066   02

Table of Contents

Enrichment
1.1 Using Division to Make Sequences

The sequence of numbers below is known as the sequence of whole numbers. At an early age, children learn to count by using whole numbers.

$$0, 1, 2, 3, 4, 5, 6, 7, 8, 9, 10, 11, 12, 13, 14, \ldots$$

When you divide each whole number by a fixed number of your choice, you can create a new sequence. The diagram at the right will help you recall the meaning of the terms related to division.

$$\begin{array}{r} 3 \leftarrow \text{quotient} \\ \text{divisor} \rightarrow 6)\overline{23} \leftarrow \text{dividend} \\ \underline{18} \\ 5 \leftarrow \text{remainder} \end{array}$$

In Exercises 1–6, consider the set of whole numbers. Write the first 10 terms of the sequence defined by the specified division.

1. the remainder you get when you divide by 1 _____

2. the remainder you get when you divide by 2 _____

3. the remainder you get when you divide by 3 _____

4. the remainder you get when you divide by 4 _____

5. the remainder you get when you divide by 5 _____

6. the remainder you get when you divide by 6 _____

7. **a.** Suppose that you divide each of the whole numbers by 12. Without writing any division or remainders, write a conjecture about the sequence of remainders that you think you will get.

   _____

   b. Write a brief justification of your conjecture from part **a.** _____

   _____

8. **a.** The following sequence of remainders is the result of dividing each whole number by an unknown number. By what number are the whole numbers being divided?

   $$0, 1, 2, 3, 4, 5, 6, 7, 8, 9, 0, 1, 2, 3, 4, 5, 6, 7, 8, 9, 0, 1, 2, 3, 4, 5, 6, 7, 8, 9, \ldots$$

   _____

   b. Write a brief justification of your conjecture from part **a.** _____

   _____

9. It is noon. Use division and remainders to find what time will be 99 hours from now. _____

   _____

Enrichment
1.2 *Sums of Counting Numbers*

One of the most notable mathematicians is Carl Frederich Gauss (1777–1855). When he was ten, his teacher assigned the problem below to his class.

Find the sum of the first 100 counting numbers.

The teacher was astonished when, in less than a minute, Gauss came up to his desk with the answer. In Exercises 1–10, you can see Gauss's reasoning and his answer.

Find the sum of each pair of vertically aligned numbers. Write the sum of each problem by using those totals. Do not actually perform the horizontal addition.

1. $1 + 2 + 3 + 4$
   $+ 4 + 3 + 2 + 1$

   _____

2. $1 + 2 + 3 + 4 + 5$
   $+ 5 + 4 + 3 + 2 + 1$

   _____

3. $1 + 2 + 3 + 4 + 5 + 6$
   $+ 6 + 5 + 4 + 3 + 2 + 1$

   _____

Write each sum in Exercises 1–3 as a product of two numbers. Do not perform the multiplication.

4. in Exercise 1

   _____ × _____

5. in Exercise 2

   _____ × _____

6. in Exercise 3

   _____ × _____

Using your answers from Exercises 4–6, find each sum.

7. $1 + 2 + 3 + 4$

   ___ × ___ ÷ ___ = ___

8. $1 + 2 + 3 + 4 + 5$

   ___ × ___ ÷ ___ = ___

9. $1 + 2 + 3 + 4 + 5 + 6$

   ___ × ___ ÷ ___ = ___

Suppose that n is a counting number of your choice. Using the process shown in Exercises 1–9, you can write a formula for the sum of the first n counting numbers.

10. **a.** Find the sum of each pair of vertically aligned numbers. Write a sum using those totals. Do not perform the addition.

   b. Use your answer to part **a** to write a formula for the sum of the first n counting numbers.

   _____

   c. Use your formula from part **b** to find the sum of the first 100 counting numbers.

   _____

11. Apply your formula from part **b** of Exercise 10 to write a formula for the sum, $2 + 4 + 6 + \ldots + 2n$.

   _____

Enrichment
1.3 Order of Operations

Some combination of the operations $+$, $-$, $\times$, and $\div$ along with grouping symbols, such as parentheses, will make the incomplete statement below into a true statement.

$$10 \; ? \; 20 \; ? \; 5 \; ? \; 2 = 12$$

One attempt to make a true statement might be to use $+$, $\div$, and $\times$, in that order.

However, when you evaluate $10 + 20 \div 5 \times 2$, you get 18, not 12.

$$
\begin{aligned}
10 + 20 \div 5 \times 2 &= 10 + 4 \times 2 \\
&= 10 + 8 \\
&= 18 \\
&\neq 12
\end{aligned}
$$

Complete Exercises 1 and 2 to determine how to make the incomplete statement above true.

1. Evaluate $(10 + 20) \div 5$. _____

2. Use operations to make $(10 \; ? \; 20) \; ? \; 5 \; ? \; 2 = 12$ true. _____

In Exercises 3–7, use only the symbols $+$, $-$, $\times$, and $\div$ to make each statement true.

3. $8 \; ? \; 3 \; ? \; 7 = 17$ _____

4. $18 \; ? \; 6 \; ? \; 2 \; ? \; 9 = 6$ _____

5. $48 \; ? \; (3 \; ? \; 2 \; ? \; 4) = 2$ _____

6. $3 \; ? \; (8 \; ? \; 2) \; ? \; 6 = 3$ _____

7. $16 \; ? \; 4 \; ? \; 3 \; ? \; 2 = 2$ _____

In Exercises 8–17, create true statements by using parentheses; the operations $+$, $-$, $\times$, and $\div$; and exactly five 3s. A statement for 0 is shown below.

$$0 = [(3 \div 3) - (3 \div 3)] \times 3$$

8. $1 =$ _____   9. $2 =$ _____

10. $3 =$ _____   11. $4 =$ _____

12. $5 =$ _____   13. $6 =$ _____

14. $7 =$ _____   15. $8 =$ _____

16. $9 =$ _____   17. $10 =$ _____

NAME _____ CLASS _____ DATE _____

Enrichment

1.4 Transforming Graphs

In the diagram at right, the small square has been transformed into the large square by multiplying the coordinates of its vertices by a definite number. Pictures, drawings, and graphics can be enlarged or reduced in this fashion.

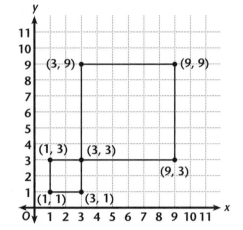

Answer each question.

1. By what number were the x- and y-coordinates of the smaller square multiplied in order to get the coordinates of the vertices of the larger square? _____

2. By what number were the x- and y-coordinates of the larger square multiplied in order to get the coordinates of the vertices of the smaller square? _____

3. Multiply the x-coordinates of the vertices of the small square by 3. Keep the y-coordinates the same. List the new coordinates. _____

4. Graph the points from Exercise 3 on a sheet of graph paper. How does multiplying the x-coordinates change the shape of the figure?

_____

5. Multiply the y-coordinates of the small square by 3. Keep the x-coordinates the same. List the new coordinates. _____

6. Graph the new coordinates from Exercise 5. How does multiplying the y-coordinates change the shape of the figure?

_____

A triangle has vertices at (2, 4), (8, 2), and (4, 6).

7. Divide the x- and y-coordinates of the vertices of the given triangle by 2. List the new coordinates. _____

8. What effect does dividing the x- and y-coordinates by 2 have on the triangle? _____

9. What is the effect of multiplying the x- and y-coordinates of the vertices of a polygon by -1?

_____

Enrichment

1.5 Exploring Maximum Volumes

Suppose that you want to make a box with an open top from a square piece of cardboard that is 10 inches on each side. The first step in making the box is to cut squares of a certain size from each corner. Once this is done, you fold the sides up and tape them so that they join.

If you let x represent the length of each side of each square, then the box will have the dimensions below.

length: $10 - 2x$ width: $10 - 2x$ height: x

In the diagram at right, you can see the box labeled with its dimensions.

To find the volume, V, of the box, substitute a value of x into the expressions for length, width, and height. Then find the value of the product of length, width, and height.

$$V = (10 - 2x)(10 - 2x)x$$

In Exercises 1–4, find the volume of the box for the given value of x.

1. $x = 1$ inch   **2.** $x = 2$ inches   **3.** $x = 3$ inches   **4.** $x = 4$ inches

_____   _____   _____   _____

Using substitution and the expressions above for length, width, and height, you can find the volume of the box for decimal values of x. To do so, you will need a calculator.

In Exercises 5–10, find the volume of the box for each value of x. Round answers to the nearest tenth.

5. $x = 1.3$ inches _____   **6.** $x = 1.4$ inches _____

7. $x = 1.5$ inches _____   **8.** $x = 1.6$ inches _____

9. $x = 1.7$ inches _____   **10.** $x = 1.8$ inches _____

11. Which of the values of x from Exercises 5–10 yields the maximum volume? _____

12. What is the maximum volume? _____

13. Find the maximum volume of a box constructed from a square sheet of cardboard with side lengths of 25 inches.

_____

Enrichment

1.6 Bounding Data With Lines

A scatter plot that represents a data set has many advantages. When you visualize the data on the coordinate plane, you can draw an inference about whether there may be a correlation, positive or negative. You may also be able to draw the inference that no correlation is apparent.

In the graph at right, you can see a scatter plot for the data set below.

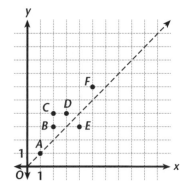

$$(1, 1), (2, 3), (2, 4), (3, 4), (4, 3), \text{ and } (5, 6)$$

The scatter plot shows a positive correlation between x and y. The points cluster closely to the line $y = x$. The greatest difference in the y-coordinates of the data points and the corresponding y-coordinates of the graph of $y = x$ is 2.

Refer to the graph above.

1. **a.** On the coordinate grid above, graph $y = x + 2$.
   b. On the coordinate grid above, graph $y = x - 1$.
   c. Do the graphs that you sketched in parts **a** and **b** bound or enclose all the given data points? Explain your response. _____

   _____

The graph at right shows a scatter plot and the line $y = x$.

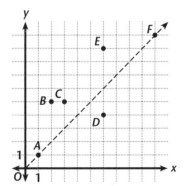

In Exercises 2 and 3, refer to the graph at right.

2. **a.** Find the greatest difference in the y-coordinates of the data points above the graph of $y = x$ and the corresponding y-coordinates of the

   graph of $y = x$. _____

   b. Find the greatest difference in the y-coordinates of the the data points below the graph of $y = x$ and the corresponding y-coordinates of the

   graph of $y = x$. _____

3. Using your answers from Exercise 2, sketch lines that are parallel to $y = x$ and that bound all the data points.

4. Explain how you can use bounding lines to analyze a data set with a positive correlation.

   _____

   _____

   _____

Enrichment

2.1 *Exploring Decimals with Patterns*

A rational number can be viewed in two ways.

• a quotient of two integers with a nonzero denominator ⟶ $\frac{3}{4}$

• a decimal that contains repeating digits ⟶ 0.01010101...

An irrational number is a decimal that is not a rational number.

When you study a decimal that repeats, you can begin to see how to create your own irrational numbers.

In Exercises 1–4, identify each decimal as rational or irrational. The bold digits provide a clue.

1. 0.**001**001001001001...

2. 0.**01001**000100001000001...

3. 0.**0102**010201020102...

4. 0.**0102001002**00010002...

In each of Exercises 5–8, you are given an irrational number whose first several digits are shown. Explain how the pattern in the digits is continued.

5. 0.120120012000...

6. 0.01001000100001000001...

7. 0.5055055505555...

8. 0.505500555000...

Sometimes you can take two irrational numbers, add them, and get a rational number as the sum. Two irrational numbers whose sum is a rational number are shown at the right.

> 0.03003000300003...
> + 0.30330333033330...

Find each sum. Write your answer as a decimal with a bar over the block of repeating digits.

9.   0.5055055505555...
    + 0.0500500050000...

10.   0.505500555000...
    + 0.161166111666...

Enrichment

2.2 *Positive and Negative Speed*

You may be surprised to learn that addition of real numbers plays a role in studying velocity problems, such as those dealing with boats traveling downstream or upstream. Notice in the diagrams below that a boat traveling downstream gets a boost from the water current; that is, speed is increased. A boat traveling upstream meets resistance from the water current; that is, speed is decreased.

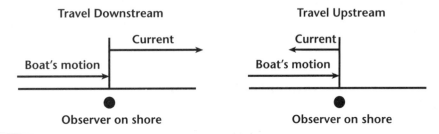

In still water, a boat travels at 12 miles per hour. Write an addition expression for the speed of the boat relative to an observer on shore.

1. downstream
   speed of water current: 4.5 miles per hour

   _____

2. upstream
   speed of water current: 1.5 miles per hour

   _____

3. upstream
   speed of water current: 15 miles per hour

   _____

4. downstream
   speed of water current: 15 miles per hour

   _____

5. A boat appears to remain still in a river whose water current has a speed of 6 miles per hour. What could you say about the speed of the boat if there were no water current?

   _____

6. A boater is traveling at 7 miles per hour in a stream whose speed is 4.5 miles per hour. Find the speed of the boat relative to an observer on shore.   _____

Tim rows at 4.5 miles per hour. Jack rows at 6.3 miles per hour in the same direction on the same river. Their speeds remain constant, but they enter a part of the river where the water current is 3.4 miles per hour. Find each speed.

7. Tim's speed relative to Jack _____

8. Jack's speed relative to Tim _____

9. Tim's parents are traveling on a road that is parallel to the river. They are driving at 45 miles per hour. If Tim is traveling upstream, how fast are they going relative to him?

   _____

Enrichment

2.3 Using Addition to Leap Over Numbers

Archimedes of Syracuse (287–212 B.C.E.) was an ingenious mathematician in ancient Greece. Storytellers recorded accounts of amazing inventions that he made in order to defeat the enemies of Greece. In the exercises that follow, you can explore a variation on a mathematical principle known as the *Axiom of Archimedes*.

Suppose that $a < b$; that is, a is to the left of b on the number line. The number-line diagram below shows that $a = 2$ and $b = 5$. It also shows that if you go to the right 2 units twice, then you will have $2 + 2 + 2 > 6$. That is, you can add a to a n times so that a leaps over b to the right.

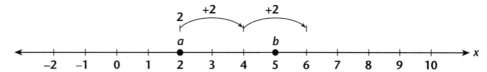

For each value of a and b, find the smallest integer n so that the sum of a with itself n times leaps over b to the right.

1. $a = 1, b = 3$ _____

2. $a = 0.5, b = 2$ _____

3. $a = 0.5, b = 4$ _____

4. $a = 0.25, b = 13$ _____

5. $a = 0.75, b = 100$ _____

6. $a = 0.75, b = 1000$ _____

Suppose that $a > b$; that is, a is to the right of b on the number line. The number-line diagram below shows that $a = 4$ and $b = -1$. It also shows that if you go to the left 4 units twice, then you will have $4 + (-4) + (-4)$ < -1. That is, you can add the opposite of a to a n times so that a leaps over b to the left.

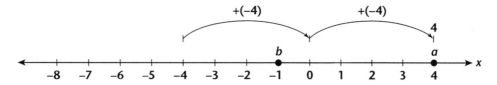

For each value of a and b, find the smallest integer n such that the sum of the opposite of a with itself n times leaps over b to the left.

7. $a = 1, b = 0$ _____

8. $a = 6, b = 2$ _____

9. $a = 1.5, b = -4$ _____

10. $a = 1, b = -13$ _____

11. $a = 100, b = -1000$ _____

12. $a = 13, b = -12$ _____

13. Let $a = 10$. When the opposite of a is added to itself 12 times, a leaps over b to the left. What value could b have? _____

Enrichment
2.4 Extending the Rules for Multiplication

In Lesson 2.4, you learned the following facts about multiplication:

• The product of two numbers with the same sign is a positive number.
• The product of two numbers with different signs is a negative number.

In the exercises that follow, you can extend what you learned to include products that involve many numbers.

In Exercises 1–6, fill in each blank space to find the product.

1. $-3 \cdot (-2) \cdot 2 = -3 \cdot [(-2) \cdot 2]$

$$= -3\left(\underline{\quad}\right)$$

$$= \underline{\quad}$$

2. $4 \cdot (-2) \cdot (-3) = 4 \cdot [(-2) \cdot (-3)]$

$$= 4\left(\underline{\quad}\right)$$

$$= \underline{\quad}$$

3. $-3 \cdot (-2) \cdot (-5) = -3 \cdot [(-2) \cdot (-5)]$

$$= -3\left(\underline{\quad}\right)$$

$$= \underline{\quad}$$

4. $5 \cdot (-2) \cdot (3) = 5 \cdot [(-2) \cdot (3)]$

$$= 5\left(\underline{\quad}\right)$$

$$= \underline{\quad}$$

5. $7 \cdot 2 \cdot 6 = 7 \cdot [2 \cdot 6]$

$$= 7\left(\underline{\quad}\right)$$

$$= \underline{\quad}$$

6. $(-10) \cdot (-2) \cdot (-5) = -10 \cdot [(-2) \cdot (-5)]$

$$= -10\left(\underline{\quad}\right)$$

$$= \underline{\quad}$$

7. Based on Exercises 1–6, write a rule for multiplying three real numbers at one time. How can you tell whether the product will be positive or negative?

_____

8. Without multiplying, tell whether the product $(-3)(-5)(3)(-10)$ will be positive or negative. _____

_____

9. Jamie needs to multiply eight real numbers. Five of them are positive numbers and three of them are negative numbers. Is the product positive or negative? Explain your reasoning.

_____

10. Suppose that n is an odd counting number. Is the product $(1)(-2)(3)(-4) \ldots (n)$ positive or negative?

_____

Enrichment

2.5 A Geometric Exploration of the Distributive Property

In the diagram at right, rectangle *ABCD* has been subdivided into four rectangles. They are rectangles *AFJE*, *EJHD*, *FBGJ*, and *JGCH*.

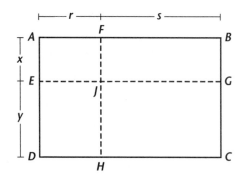

Recall that the area of a rectangle is expressed as follows:

Area = length × width

Find the area of each rectangular region in terms of the lengths, *r* and *s*, and the widths, *x* and *y*.

1. region *AFJE* _____

2. region *FBGJ* _____

3. region *EJHD* _____

4. region *JGCH* _____

Refer to your answers to Exercises 1–4.

5. a. Using your answers to Exercises 1 and 2, write a sum and a product for the area of region *ABGE*. _____

b. Write an equation relating the two expressions that you found in part **a**. _____

c. What property of real numbers do your answers to parts **a** and **b** confirm? _____

In the exercises that follow, you can see how to expand the product $(x + y)(r + s)$, which represents the area of rectangle *ABCD*.

6. a. Write the area of rectangle *ABCD* as the sum of the areas of two rectangular regions, region *ABGE* and region *EGCD*.

_____

b. Using your answer to part **a**, explain how to write $(x + y)(r + s)$ as a sum of four expressions.

_____

c. Write the area of rectangle *ABCD* as the sum of the areas of two rectangular regions, region *AFHD* and region *FBCH*.

_____

d. Using your answer to part **c**, explain how to write $(x + y)(r + s)$ as a sum of four expressions.

_____

Enrichment

2.6 Perimeter of Oddly Shaped Regions

In science and industry, scale drawings are used to represent objects. The scale drawing can represent an enlargement of a small object, such as a computer chip, or a reduction of a large object, such as the floor plan of a house.

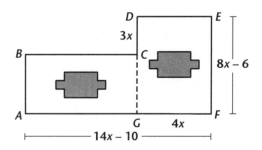

The diagram at right is a scale drawing that represents the top view of a machine part. The actual dimensions of the part are three times those found in the scale drawing.

Notice that the boundary of the drawing consists of six line segments joined at their endpoints. However, only four of those segments have measurements marked.

Write an expression for each length.

1. AB _____

2. BC _____

3. DE _____

4. a. The perimeter of the scale drawing is the distance around its boundary. Write an expression in simplified form for the perimeter of the drawing.

_____

b. Given your answer to Part a and $x = 4$, find the perimeter of the scale drawing.

_____

The diagram at the right shows a scale drawing of the top view of a machine part.

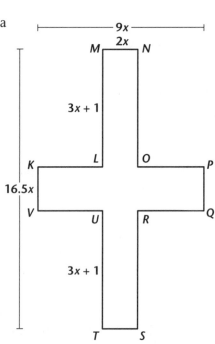

5. If $KL = OP = VU = RQ$, write and simplify one expression for these four lengths. _____

6. If $KV = PQ$, write and simplify one expression for these two lengths. _____

7. Using the given measurements and your answers from Exercises 5 and 6, write and simplify an expression for the perimeter of the scale drawing. _____

8. Given your answer to Exercise 7 and $x = 4$, find the perimeter of the scale drawing. _____

A rule from geometry relates the perimeter of a scale drawing to the perimeter of the actual object. If the scale is 1 unit : n units, then the perimeter of the actual object is n times that of the scale drawing.

9. The scale is 1 unit : 12 units. Given this fact and $x = 4$, find the perimeter of the top view of the actual machine part. _____

Enrichment

2.7 *Area of an Algebraic Region*

Sometimes it is necessary to find the area of a border, the region that surrounds a figure. One way to calculate the area of a border is to use the formula for the area of a rectangle twice.

To find the area of a rectangle, multiply the length by the width. Using this idea, can you devise a method to calculate the area of the shaded region in the figure at right?

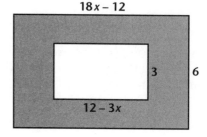

Refer to the diagram at right above.

1. a. Write an expression for the area of the large rectangle. Then simplify.

_____

b. Write an expression for the area of the small rectangle. Then simplify.

_____

c. Use your answers to parts **a** and **b** to write and simplify an expression for the area of the shaded region.

_____

2. Suppose that the diagram above represents a plot of land with the specified dimensions and x equal to 250. Explain why your answer to part **c** of Exercise 1 makes the calculation of the area of the shaded region simpler than finding the area directly from the given dimensions.

_____

The diagram at right shows a rectangular region with one shaded square inside it.

3. Suppose that you want to place as many of the shaded squares as possible inside the rectangular region in such a way that the squares touch one another and do not overlap. What is the maximum number of shaded squares that you can use to accomplish this?

_____

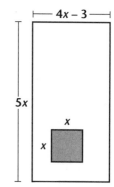

4. Given your answer to Exercise 3, write an expression for the unshaded region inside the rectangle.

_____

5. Suppose that the dimensions of the rectangle above are doubled but the dimensions of the shaded square are kept the same. Write the new dimensions of both figures.

_____

6. a. Find the maximum number of shaded squares that you can arrange inside the rectangular region.

_____

b. Given your answer to part **a**, write an expression for the area of the region that is left unshaded.

_____

Enrichment
3.1 Rate Problems

The function of an odometer is to measure the distance that a vehicle has traveled, either in miles or in kilometers. When you use an odometer for this purpose, you can answer the question, "How far have I traveled?" The reasoning that you used to answer the question can be applied to stating and solving new related problems.

Answer the following questions.

1. You are on a trip traveling from town A to town B. When you start the trip, your odometer reading is 37,538 miles. When you get to town B, your odometer reading is 37,781 miles.
   a. Write an equation relating your initial reading, distance traveled,

      and final reading. _____

   b. Find the distance traveled from town A to town B. _____

2. Let s represent the initial reading, d represent the distance traveled, and e represent the final reading. Write an addition equation relating

   s, d, and e. _____

3. Using your equation from Exercise 2, solve for the specified variable.

   a. $s =$ _____   b. $d =$ _____   c. $e =$ _____

4. Use one of the equations that you wrote in Exercise 3 and the given values to find the value of the third variable.
   a. $s = 27{,}281$ and $e = 28{,}978$ b. $e = 17{,}439$ and $d = 197$

   _____   _____

   c. $s = 62{,}979$ and $d = 798$ d. $s = 69{,}876$ and $e = 70{,}987$

   _____   _____

The water level in a storage tank is currently $10\frac{1}{2}$ feet.

5. Water is drained from the tank, and the level drops $2\frac{5}{6}$ feet. Find the

   new water level. _____

6. Let o represent the original water level, d represent the change in water level, and f represent the final water level. Write three equations

   relating o, d, and f. _____

7. The water level rises $1\frac{3}{4}$ feet from $7\frac{2}{3}$ feet. Choose an equation from

   Exercise 6 and find the new water level.   _____

Enrichment

3.2 Deriving the Division Property of Equality

The Multiplication Property of Equality states that if a, b, and c are numbers and $a = b$, then $ac = bc$. That is, when you multiply each side of an equation by a fixed number, the resulting products are equal.

By itself, you can use the Multiplication Property of Equality to solve equations of the form $ax = b$ as well as equations of the form $\frac{x}{a} = b$. You can see this fact at work in the solution below.

$$3x = 6$$
$$\frac{1}{3}(3x) = \frac{1}{3}(6)$$
$$\left[\frac{1}{3}(3)\right]x = \frac{1}{3}(6)$$
$$1x = \frac{1}{3}(6)$$
$$x = 2$$

Notice that you multiply by a fraction whose numerator is 1, that is, by the reciprocal of a.

Solve each equation by using only the Multiplication Property of Equality. Show your work.

1. $4x = 12$ _____

2. $-3x = 15$ _____

3. $-7x = -21$ _____

4. $10t = 12$ _____

5. $18w = 9$ _____

6. $-3d = -90$ _____

7. Suppose that $a \neq 0$. Using the process that you followed in Exercises 1–6,

   solve $ax = b$ for x. _____

8. Use the Division Property of Equality to solve $ax = b$ for x. _____

9. Compare the method of solving an equation of the form $ax = b$ by using the Multiplication Property of Equality with that of solving the same type of equation by using the Division Property of Equality.

   _____

   _____

Enrichment

3.3 Using Two-Step Equations to Solve Geometry Problems

Many concepts of algebra can be applied to a wide range of geometry problems.

Suppose that you want to design a box. The base of the box will be a square that is 10 inches on each side, and the box will be h inches tall. The surface area of the box (that is, the area of cardboard needed to make the box, assuming no overlap) is given by $4 \cdot 10 \cdot h + 2 \cdot 10 \cdot 10$, or $40h + 200$. For a surface area of 360 square inches, you would solve $40h + 200 = 360$ in order to find the height of the box.

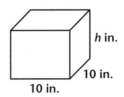

The base of a rectangular box is to be a square that is 10 inches on each side. For each given surface area, find the corresponding height of the box.

1. 360 square inches _____

2. 520 square inches _____

3. 240 square inches _____

4. 560 square inches _____

5. 800 square inches _____

6. 480 square inches _____

Now suppose that you want to design a cylindrical box whose base is a circle with a radius of 5 inches. The surface area of the cylindrical box is given by $50\pi + 10\pi h$.

The base of a cylindrical box will be a circle with a radius of 5 inches. For each given surface area, find the corresponding height of the box.

7. 80π square inches _____

8. 120π square inches _____

9. 110π square inches _____

10. 160π square inches _____

11. 200π square inches _____

12. 90π square inches _____

Another geometric application of two-step equations relates to the interior angles of a polygon. If the polygon has n sides, the sum of the measures of its angles is $180n - 360$ degrees.

$$\begin{array}{cc} 120° & 110° \\ 60° & 70° \end{array}$$

For example, in a triangle, $n = 3$, so the measures of the angles add up to 180°. For a trapezoid, $n = 4$, so the measures of the angles add up to 360°.

In the following exercises, the sum of the measures of the interior angles of a polygon is given. Find the number of sides of the polygon.

13. 540° _____

14. 1800° _____

15. 900° _____

16. 2880° _____

Enrichment

3.4 Finding a Formula to Solve Linear Equations

A linear equation in one variable can take on many different appearances. Each of the equations below is an equation in one variable.

$2x - 5 = 12$ $2(x + 1) = 5$ $3x - 4 = -2x + 1$

Although these equations look different, you can transform each of them into the standard form for a linear equation in one variable.

In Exercises 1–4, each equation has the form $ax + b = 0$. Solve each equation.

1. $3x + 7 = 0$ _____

2. $-2x - 8 = 0$ _____

3. $\frac{2}{3}x - 5 = 0$ _____

4. $-4.1x - 8.2 = 0$ _____

You can always transform a given linear equation in one variable into the form $ax + b = 0$.

In Exercises 5–8, write each equation in the form $ax + b = 0$. Do not solve the resulting equation.

5. $3(x + 5) = x + 21$

_____

6. $-2(-4 - 6x) = -10 + 3x$

_____

7. $-7(-3 - x) = -2(3 - x)$

_____

8. $8 - 2(x - 5) = x - 3$

_____

9. a. Solve $ax + b = 0$ for x. _____

   b. Explain how to write your answer to part **a** as a formula that you can use to solve a linear equation in x.

   _____

Solve the specified equation by using your formula from Exercise 9.

10. Exercise 5 _____

11. Exercise 6 _____

12. Exercise 7 _____

13. Exercise 8 _____

14. a. Let $ax + b = 0$, where $a = 0$ and $b = 0$. How many solutions does the equation have?

   _____

   b. Let $ax + b = 0$, where $a = 0$ and $b \neq 0$. How many solutions does the equation have?

   _____

Enrichment

3.5 Ancient Solution Methods

The *Bakhshuli Manuscript,* which was written by an unknown author hundreds of years ago, was discovered in northwest India in 1881. The manuscript poses the following problem:

> A merchant pays a duty on certain goods at three different places. At the first place, he gives $\frac{1}{3}$ of the goods, at the second place $\frac{1}{4}$ of the remainder, and at the third place $\frac{1}{5}$ of the remainder. The total duty is 24 goods. What was the original number of his goods?

The solution according to the manuscript is as follows:

> Having subtracted the series from 1, we get $\frac{2}{3}$, $\frac{3}{4}$, and $\frac{4}{5}$. These multiplied together give $\frac{2}{5}$. That subtracted from 1 gives $\frac{3}{5}$. The total duty, 24, is divided by $\frac{3}{5}$, giving 40, which is the original amount.

1. To solve this problem algebraically, let x be the original number of goods. Complete the table.

	Original amount	First location	Second location	Third location
Duty paid	0			
Remaining goods	x			

One equation that models this problem is

$$\frac{1}{3}x + \frac{1}{4}\left(1 - \frac{1}{3}\right)x + \frac{1}{5}\left(1 - \frac{1}{4}\right)\left(1 - \frac{1}{3}\right)x = 24, \quad \text{or} \quad \frac{1}{3}x + \frac{1}{4} \cdot \frac{2}{3}x + \frac{1}{5} \cdot \frac{3}{4} \cdot \frac{2}{3}x = 24.$$

2. Use the Distributive Property to solve this equation. _____

The Hindu mathematician Mahavira (850 A.D.) wrote an elementary mathematics book containing the following problem:

> Of a collection of mango fruits, the king took $\frac{1}{6}$, the queen took $\frac{1}{5}$ of the remainder, the three chief princes took $\frac{1}{4}$, $\frac{1}{3}$, and $\frac{1}{2}$ of the successive remainders, and the youngest child took the remaining three mangoes. Oh, you who are clever in miscellaneous problems on fractions, give out the measure of that collection of mangoes.

3. Write and solve an equation for finding the total number of mangoes.

Equation: _____ Solution: _____

4. Which method do you prefer for solving these problems—the method used in the Bakhshuli Manuscript, or modern algebraic methods? Explain.

_____

_____

Enrichment

3.6 A Formula of Interest

When you put your money in a savings account, the bank may pay you *simple interest*. Let P represent the dollar amount of your deposit (the principal), let r represent the interest rate, and let t represent the number of years. The amount of interest you earn, I, is given by the *simple interest formula*: $I = Prt$.

Note that banks typically use percents to describe their interest rates. Percent means "per hundred," so an interest rate of 5% means that you should use $r = \frac{5}{100}$, or 0.05.

Use the simple interest formula to solve the following problems:

1. If $P = 2500$, $r = 0.03$, and $t = 5$, what is I? _____

2. If $r = 0.025$, $t = 3$, and $I = 150$, what is P? _____

3. If $P = 500$, $r = 0.06$, and $I = 150$, what is t? _____

4. If $P = 3000$, $t = 4$, and $I = 384$, what is r? _____

5. Kevin is making a deposit of $1800 at his local bank. The bank pays 6.5% simple interest ($r = 0.065$). If Kevin leaves his deposit at the bank for 3 years, how much interest will he earn? _____

6. Cecelia made a deposit of $600 at a bank paying 4% simple interest ($r = 0.04$). How long should she leave her deposit at the bank in order to earn $72 in interest? _____

7. Darryl opened an account at a bank which paid 5.5% simple interest ($r = 0.055$). After 6 years, he had earned $726 in interest. What was the amount of his original deposit? _____

8. Sophia deposited $150 at a savings and loan association paying simple interest. If she earned $27 in interest after 6 years, what was the interest rate? _____

9. Nathan made a deposit of $650 at a bank paying 3.8% simple interest ($r = 0.038$). If he leaves his deposit at the bank for 10 years, how much interest will he earn? _____

10. Susie made a deposit of $980 at a credit union paying 7% simple interest ($r = 0.07$). How long should she leave her deposit at the credit union in order to earn $343 in interest? _____

11. Guillermo deposited $1350 at a bank paying simple interest. If he earned $109.35 in 3 years, what was the interest rate? _____

Enrichment

4.1 Using Cross Products to Derive New Proportions

In Lesson 4.1, you learned that in a true proportion, the cross products are equal.

$$\frac{a}{b} = \frac{c}{d}$$

If $\frac{a}{b} = \frac{c}{d}$, then $ad = bc$.

The proof to the statement above is shown at right.

$bd\left(\frac{a}{b}\right) = bd\left(\frac{c}{d}\right)$ Multiplication Property of Equality

$da = bc$ Inverse Property of Multiplication

$ad = bc$ Commutative Property of Multiplication

Using $\frac{a}{b} = \frac{c}{d}$, you can write and prove that other proportions involving

$a, b, c,$ and d are true.

In each proportion, assume that the denominator is not equal to 0.

1. Let $\frac{a}{b} = \frac{c}{d}$, where $a = 5$, $b = 7$, $c = 15$, and $d = 21$. Verify that

    the product of the means is equal to the product of the extremes. _____

2. **a.** Let $\frac{a}{b} = \frac{c}{d}$. What can be done to each side of $\frac{a}{b} = \frac{c}{d}$ in order to get $\frac{d}{c} = \frac{b}{a}$? _____

    b. Justify each step in the reasoning below in order to show that $\frac{d}{c} = \frac{b}{a}$.

    $\frac{a}{b} = \frac{c}{d}$

    $ad = bc$ _____

    $\left(\frac{1}{ac}\right)ad = \left(\frac{1}{ac}\right)bc$ _____

    $\frac{d}{c} = \frac{b}{a}$ _____

3. Let $\frac{a}{b} = \frac{c}{d}$. Show that $\frac{d}{b} = \frac{c}{a}$. Write your reasons to the right of your steps.

    _____

    _____

    _____

For Exercises 4 and 5, let $\frac{a}{b} = \frac{c}{d}$. Verify each proportion. Then try to justify your conclusion.

4. $\frac{a + b}{b} = \frac{c + d}{d}$ 5. $\frac{a - b}{b} = \frac{c - d}{d}$

Enrichment

4.2 Markup and Markdown

During a sale, the markdown of an item often becomes the focal point of the advertisement, such as "25% off". When you save 25%, or $\frac{1}{4}$, of the cost of the item, you pay $1 - \frac{1}{4}$, or $\frac{3}{4}$, of the cost. Frequently, a markup on an item is made before a sale starts. If an item is marked up by 25%, or $\frac{1}{4}$, the new cost becomes $1 + \frac{1}{4}$, or $\frac{5}{4}$, of the old cost.

In the exercises below, a coat originally costs $130.

1. The merchant marks the coat up by 25%. Find the new price of the coat. _____

2. After the markup is made, the merchant marks the coat down by 40%. Find the sale price of the coat after it is marked up and then marked down. _____

3. Chris thought that the sale price of the coat after the markup and then the markdown should result in a 15% reduction in the original cost of the coat. Use reasoning to show that this is not correct.

   _____

4. In the box at right, a three-step process has taken place. Given your work in Exercises 1 and 2, describe the process.

   _____

   _____

Step 1: 240
Step 2: $\left(1 + \frac{3}{10}\right)240$
Step 3: $\left(1 - \frac{15}{100}\right)\left[\left(1 + \frac{3}{10}\right)240\right]$

5. An item is marked up by a given percent and is then marked down by a given percent. Explain how to find the sale price?

   _____

In some sale situations, a merchant will mark an item down and then mark the item down again.

6. Find the sale price of the coat after a 25% markdown. _____

7. After the markdown in Exercise 6, the merchant marked the item down 40%. Find the sale price after the second markdown. _____

8. In the box at right, a three-step process has taken place. Given your work in Exercises 6 and 7, describe the process.

   _____

   _____

Step 1: 130
Step 2: $\left(1 - \frac{3}{10}\right)130$
Step 3: $\left(1 - \frac{15}{100}\right)\left[\left(1 - \frac{3}{10}\right)130\right]$

9. Explain how to find the sale price of an item after it is marked down by a given percent and then marked down by another percent.

   _____

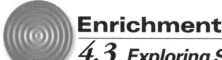

Enrichment

4.3 *Exploring Solution Likelihoods*

Probability was not studied formally until the seventeenth century when Blaise Pascal (1623–1662) and Pierre de Fermat (1601?–1665) began a correspondence with each other concerning various problems in gambling. One method of probability that has since been employed is the usage of a probability bar.

A probability bar extends from 0 to 1. These numbers represent impossibility and certainty, respectively.

0.0	0.25	0.5	0.75	1.0

In Exercises 1–3, use the ratio $\dfrac{\text{number of favorable outcomes}}{\text{number of total outcomes}}$.

1. Explain why a probability must be a nonnegative number. _____

2. How does the ratio above tell you that a probability must be between 0 and 1 inclusive?

_____

3. Explain how 0.25, 0.5, and 0.75 divide the probability bar into sections.

_____

Rather than use a problem-solving strategy, Debbie tried to guess at a solution to an inequality that was given to her. Her guesses are -4, -3, -2, -1, 0, 1, 2, 3, 4, 5, 6, 7, and 8.

In Exercises 4–9, find the probability that a number selected at random from the list above will be a solution to the given inequality. Rate her probability of success.

4. $4n - 3 \geq 25$

_____

5. $4n - 3 \geq 17$

_____

6. $4n - 3 \geq 5$

_____

7. $4n - 3 \geq -11$

_____

8. $4n - 3 \geq 45$

_____

9. $4n - 3 \geq -27$

_____

10. Write an inequality for which Debbie's probability of success will be at least 50%.

_____

Enrichment

4.4 Finding the Mean and Median for Patterned Lists

In Lesson 4.4, you learned how to find the mean and median of a data set. For certain data sets, those that exhibit a pattern, you may be able to write special rules to help find statistical measures.

In Exercises 1–4, mentally find the mean and median of each data set.

1. 1, 2, 3, 4, and 5 _____

2. 72, 73, and 74 _____

3. 9, 10, 11, 12, and 13 _____

4. 36, 36, 42, and 42 _____

In Exercises 5–7, consider the data set 5, 6, 7, and 8.

5. Find the mean. _____

6. Find the median. _____

7. Calculate the average of the first and last terms in the list. _____

In Exercises 8–10, consider the data set 7, 8, 9, and 10.

8. Find the mean. _____

9. Find the median. _____

10. Calculate the average of the first and last terms in the list. _____

11. Based on your work in Exercises 5–10, write rules, using the first and last numbers in a data set that consists of consecutive integers, to find the mean and median of the data set.

_____

Using your response to Exercise 11, find the mean and median of each problem.

12. 32, 33, 34, . . . , 96 _____

13. 2, 1, 0, . . . , -12 _____

14. 20, 19, 8, . . . , 0 _____

15. $-3, -4, -5, . . . , -6$ _____

In Exercises 16 and 17, you can try to extend your rules for finding the mean and median to data sets that have a constant first difference other than 1 or -1.

16. a. Find the mean and median of the data set 11, 13, 15, 17, and 19. _____

b. Do your rules from Exercise 11 give you the correct mean and median. Explain your response.

_____

17. Write rules for finding the mean and median of $a, a + 3, a + 6, a + 9, . . . , a + 3(k - 1)$, where k is a positive integer.

_____

Enrichment

4.5 Exploring Pictographs

To make a data set more meaningful, it is sometimes useful to represent it in a *pictograph*. A pictograph uses pictures or symbols to represent data. Each pictograph has a key that indicates the number of data items represented by each symbol. Usually the numbers that the symbols represent are approximated or rounded. The value of each row in a pictograph is the product of the number of symbols in the row, including fractional symbols, and the value of the symbol given in the key.

A pictograph is especially useful when you want to represent data visually. For this reason, pictographs are found quite often in reports, presentations, magazines, and newspapers.

In Exercises 1–5, use the pictograph below.

Students With Part-Time Jobs

Fast-food restaurant	☐ ☐ ☐
Convenience store	☐ ☐ ☐ ☐
Supermarket	☐ ☐ ☐
Baby-sitting	☐ ☐ ☐ ☐ ☐ ☐ ☐
Newspaper delivery	☐ ☐

Key: Each ☐ represents 10 students.

1. How many students earn money by working in a fast-food restaurant?

2. In which category does the smallest number of students work? How many work in this category?

3. How many students work in fast-food restaurants and convenience stores?

4. Which job has 25 more students than those in newspaper delivery?

5. How many more students earn money by baby-sitting than by working at the supermarket?

Raul plays on the high-school basketball team.
The table shows his scores over a seven-game period.

Game	1	2	3	4	5	6	7
Number of points	14	21	15	12	4	19	26

6. In the space at right, construct a pictograph showing Raul's scores. Use a basketball as the symbol and choose the number of points that one basketball represents.

Enrichment

4.6 Contrasting Central Tendency With Spread of Data

A box-and-whisker plot helps you see how data are distributed, that is, the relationship between the greatest and least values as well as the relationship among the quartiles.

In Exercises 1–8, refer to the quiz-score data below.

Quiz scores: Bob   3, 5, 7, 8, 8, 11
            Jean   5, 6, 7, 8, 8, 9

1. Find the mean, median, and mode(s) of Bob's scores. _____

2. Find the mean, median, and mode(s) of Jean's scores. _____

3. Do the measures of central tendency tell you anything about the spread of data for each student? Explain your response.

4. In the space provided, make a box-and-whisker plot for each data set. Place one over the other.

5. What do you notice about the two boxes of the plots? _____

6. What do you notice about the whiskers of the plots? _____

7. Describe how the box-and-whisker plots for Bob and Jean differ.

   _____

8. What is the advantage of using a box-and-whisker plot instead of using just the three measures of central tendency?

   _____

Refer to the box-and-whisker plot at right.

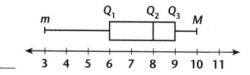

9. Write a seven-number data set that can be represented by the plot at right. _____

10. Explain why you cannot find the mean of a data set from its box-and-whisker plot.

    _____

Enrichment

5.1 Exploring Algebraic and Geometric Functions

A function is a correspondence, *f*, between two sets, *A* and *B*, such that each member of *A* is assigned exactly one member of *B*. The diagram shows a function as a dynamic process.

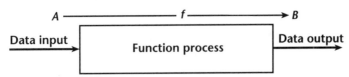

In Exercises 1–3, suppose that the input set, *A*, is the set of integers. Describe the range of each function.

1. *f*: Multiply each integer, *n*, by 5.   _____

2. *g*: Multiply each integer, *n*, by a fixed integer, *k*.   _____

3. *h*: Divide the input integer, *n*, by 10 and write the reaminder, *r*.   _____

In Exercises 4–6, write a function rule that represents the function described.

4. *j*: the coordinate of the point halfway between each distinct pair of points on a number line   _____

5. *k*: the distance of each point from 0   _____

6. *m*: the length of the line segment determined by each distinct pair of points on the number line   _____

In Exercises 7 and 8, the domain of each function is the set of all squares.

7. **a.** Write a function, *P*, that gives the perimeter of any square.   _____

   b. Write a function, *A*, that gives the area of any square.   _____

8. **a.** Using the diagram at right, describe the function that moves the square from A to B.

   _____

   b. What is the range of the function in part **a**?

   _____

9. Suppose that you roll two number cubes. The sum of the numbers that are showing can be represented by a function.
   a. In the space at the right, make a table showing the members of the domain.

   b. What is the range of the function? _____

Enrichment

5.2 *Exploring the Meaning of a Difference Quotient*

When two variables x and y are related and (x_1, y_1) and (x_2, y_2) satisfy the relationship, you can write the quotient as shown at right. The quotient is called a *difference quotient*.

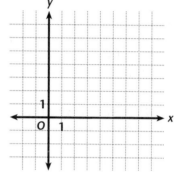

$$\frac{y_2 - y_1}{x_2 - x_1}$$

The difference quotient can have different meanings in different situations.

In Exercises 1–5, use the grid at the right.

1. Graph and connect $A(-2, -3)$, $B(1, 3)$, and $C(3, 7)$.

2. Calculate the slope of $\overline{AB}$ and of $\overline{BC}$. _____

3. On the same grid, graph $D(2, 6)$. Connect A, B and D.

4. Calculate the slope of $\overline{AB}$ and of $\overline{BD}$. _____

5. Explain how to use a difference quotient to determine whether three points are collinear, that is, whether three points lie on the same line.

_____

Another application of the difference quotient is the measurement of the *grade*, or steepness, of a road. A grade of 3% means that the road surface rises 3 feet for every horizontal run of 100 feet. A roadway that slopes down has a negative grade.

6. If the vertical rise of a highway is 150 feet when the horizontal run is 5000 feet, what is the grade of the road? _____

7. If the grade of a road is 5%, what is the vertical rise of the road when the horizontal run is 6000 feet? _____

8. On a certain stretch of road, the point 420 feet east of point A is 24 feet lower than point A. Point B, 600 feet east of A, is 36 feet lower than point A.

   a. Find the grade of the road surface between points A and B. _____

   b. Would a motorist driving along a stretch of road from point B to point A report the same grade for the road as a motorist driving from A to B would report? Explain your response.

_____

In economics, the additional cost to produce one more unit of an item is called the *marginal cost* of the item. Marginal cost is found by computing

the difference quotient, or $\dfrac{\text{difference in manufacturing cost}}{\text{difference in units made}}$.

9. The cost that a manufacturer pays for producing 5 pairs of shoes is $113. The cost for 12 pairs of shoes is $127. Use a difference quotient to find the marginal cost, or manufacturing cost, per pair of shoes. _____

Enrichment

5.3 Combining Direct-Variation Relationships

In Lesson 5.3, you learned that when y varies directly as x, there is a nonzero number, k, such that $y = kx$. There are many situations in which one variable varies directly with another variable.

A 700-gallon tank contains 500 gallons of a certain liquid. Three pumps feed three different ingredients into the tank at its top. A discharge pump at the base of the tank removes the mixed ingredients. The rates at which the pipes feed and remove liquid are shown at right.

Pump 1:	5 gallons per minute
Pump 2:	10 gallons per minute
Pump 3:	15 gallons per minute
Discharge pump:	35 gallons per minute

Let t represent the amount of time for which each pipe is operating.

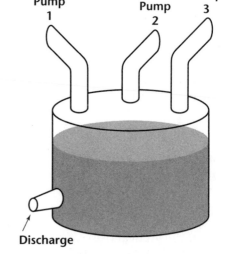

1. Write a direct-variation relationship for the gallons supplied by each pump. Then find the amount of time that it takes for each pump to fill the tank to capacity if each works alone.

   a. pump 1 _____

   b. pump 2 _____

   c. pump 3 _____

2. On certain occasions, some pumps are turned on at the same time. Write a direct-variation relationship for each combination of pumps operating simultaneously.

   a. pump 1 and pump 2   _____

   b. pump 2 and pump 3   _____

   c. pump 1, pump 2, and pump 3 _____

3. At noon, the tank contains 500 gallons of solution. At noon, all pumps, and the discharge pump, are turned on simultaneously.

   a. Write an equation for the quantity, Q, of solution t minutes after noon. _____

   b. Is the tank filling or emptying? At what rate is this happening? _____

   c. After how many minutes will the tank be full or empty? _____

4. At noon, the tank contains 500 gallons of solution and all feeder pumps are turned on. At 12:06 P.M., the discharge pump is turned on.

   a. Write an equation or equations for the quantity, Q, of solution t minutes after noon. _____

   b. How many minutes after noon will the tank either be full or be empty? _____

Enrichment

5.4 Continuing a Line by Using Little Information

A point on a line and its slope tell you everything you need to know about the line. In the diagram at right, the slope, $-\frac{2}{3}$, and the point P can be used to locate point Q. On the other hand, point Q and the slope, $-\frac{2}{3}$, can be used to locate point P.

Here are some questions that you can ask and answer by using a small amount of information about a line.
1. Where does the line cross the y-axis?
2. Where does the line cross the y-axis if you are given the coordinates of two points rather than the coordinates of one point and a slope?

Refer to the graph at right above.

1. **a.** Write the coordinates of point P. _____

   b. Write the coordinates of the point that you would get if you started at P and followed the pattern suggested in the diagram. _____

   c. Find the coordinates of the point where the line crosses the y-axis. _____

2. Find the coordinates of the point where the line crosses the x-axis. _____

A line contains $A(9, 8)$ and has a slope of $\frac{2}{3}$. Use this information in Exercises 3 and 4.

3. Find the coordinates of the point where the line crosses the y-axis. _____

4. Find the coordinates of the point where the line crosses the x-axis. _____

A line contains points $K(-6, 4)$ and $L(-3, 2)$. Use this information in Exercises 5–7.

5. Graph points K and L on the grid at right.

6. Find the coordinates of the point where the line containing these points crosses the y-axis. _____

7. Find the coordinates of the point where the line containing these points crosses the x-axis. _____

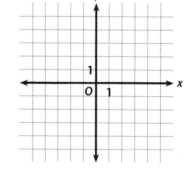

8. A line contains $R(12, 20)$ and $S(14, 23)$. Find the coordinates of the point that you get when you start at R and apply the slope to R ten times backward to the left. _____

Enrichment

5.5 Searching for Integer Solutions

The equation $4x + 3y = 12$ represents a linear equation in x and y. Its graph is shown at right. Notice that x may be any real number and that y may be any real number. The graph also shows that $(3, 0)$ and $(0, 4)$ are points on the graph with integer coordinates.

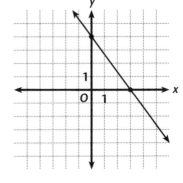

One question that you can ask about $4x + 3y = 12$ is whether there are other ordered pairs that satisfy the equation and that have integer coordinates.

Consider $4x + 3y = 12$.

1. Use trial and error to find two other ordered pairs that satisfy the equation and that have integer coordinates. _____

2. **a.** Verify that if $4x + 3y = 12$, then $y = -\dfrac{4x}{3} + 4$.

   b. Using the form that you verified in part **a**, experiment to find two ordered pairs, different from those given above and different from those you found in part **a**, that satisfy the equation and have integer coordinates. _____

   c. Let x be an integer. What can you say about y if x is a multiple of 3? if x is not a multiple of 3?

   _____

Sometimes, when you transform an equation from standard form to slope-intercept form, the y-intercept will not be an integer.

Consider $4x + 5y = 12$.

3. **a.** Verify that if $4x + 5y = 12$, then $y = \dfrac{-4x + 12}{5}$.

   _____

   b. Suppose that you choose x to be an integer. Let $x = -5, -4, -3, -2, -1, 0, 1, 2, 3, 4,$ and 5. Which of these values of x gives integer values of y? Write a rule that tells which values of x give integer values of y.

   _____

4. Let $3x + 7y = 20$. Write a rule that tells which values of x will give integer values of y.

   _____

Enrichment

5.6 Constructing Polygons Using Parallel and Perpendicular Lines

Two facts about parallel and perpendicular lines are summarized below.

> If two nonvertical lines are parallel, then their slopes are equal.
>
> If two nonvertical lines are perpendicular, then their slopes are negative reciprocals of one another.

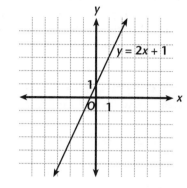

You can use these facts if you want to construct special polygons on the coordinate plane.

In Exercises 1–4, use the grid and the graph of $y = 2x + 1$.

1. **a.** Write an equation in slope-intercept form for the line parallel to the graph of $y = 2x + 1$ and having a y-intercept of 4.

   b. Graph your equation on the grid at right above.

2. **a.** Find the y-coordinate of the point on the graph of $y = 2x + 1$ for which $x = -2$.

   b. Find an equation for the line containing the point found in Part a and perpendicular to the graph of $y = 2x + 1$.

   c. Graph your equation from Part b on the grid at right above.

3. **a.** Find the y-coordinate of the point on the graph of $y = 2x + 1$ for which $x = 1$.

   b. Find an equation for the line containing the point found in Part a and perpendicular to the graph of $y = 2x + 1$.

   c. Graph your equation from Part b on the grid at right above.

4. Identify the polygon that you formed. Explain your response.

_____

In Exercises 5 and 6, use the grid at right.

5. Suppose that you want to make a square using the graph of $x + y = 4$ to help determine one side of the square.

Write equations in standard form to determine a square with corners at $(4, 0)$, $(0, 4)$, $(-4, 0)$ and $(0, -4)$.

6. On the grid at right, graph each of the equations that you wrote in Exercise 5.

Enrichment

6.1 *Solving Garden Problems Using Inequalities*

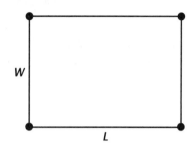

Susan has 200 feet of fencing and wants to use it to enclose a rectangular garden. She knows that the formula for the perimeter of a rectangle is $P = 2(L + W)$. Susan also knows that the area A of a rectangle is found by using $A = LW$.

Answer the following questions in order to help Susan plan how to use the fencing.

1. Susan can either use some or all of the fencing. Write an inequality that describes how much fencing she could use.   _____

2. Would a length of 70 feet and a width of 40 feet satisfy the inequality in Exercise 1? Explain.

_____

3. **a.** If Susan decides to use all of the fencing and chooses a length of 20 feet, find the width.   _____

   b. What would the length be if she chooses a width of 20 feet?   _____

   c. Given these dimensions, find the area of the garden.   _____

4. **a.** If Susan decides to use all of the fencing and chooses a length of 40 feet, find the width.   _____

   b. What would the length be if she chooses a width of 40 feet?   _____

   c. Given these dimensions, find the area of the garden.   _____

5. What conclusion can you draw from Exercises 3 and 4?

_____

6. **a.** If Susan would like the length and the width to be as close to one another as possible and to be whole numbers, what might the dimensions be?   _____

   b. Given her intention in part **a**, what shape is she trying to achieve?   _____

   c. Given your answer to part **a**, find the area of the garden.   _____

7. Susan's friend, Jack, has 160 feet of fencing. He wants to use all his fencing to make a garden with the greatest possible area. Without using inequalities, what dimensions should he choose?   _____

Enrichment

6.2 Using Multiple Inequalities

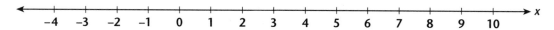

As you have already seen, when you solve a linear equation, you find a definite value. If the variable is equal to 3, then the number line is divided into three parts: the number 3, those numbers greater than 3, and those numbers less than 3. When you deal with multiple inequalities, you divide the number line into even more parts.

In Exercises 1–4, use the number line below.

```
  ←——+——+——+——+——+——+——+——+——+——+——+——+——+——+——+——→ x
    -4  -3  -2  -1   0   1   2   3   4   5   6   7   8   9  10
```

1. Draw a graph showing the solutions to $x \geq 3$ and $x < 7$.

2. What integers satisfy both of these inequalities?   _____

3. What inequalities describe your response in Exercise 2?   _____

On a certain freeway, the minimum allowable speed is 40 miles per hour, and the maximum allowable speed is 55 miles per hour.

Use the information above to answer Exercises 4–6.

4. Write an inequality for each driving situation.
   a. A motorist is driving too fast.   _____

   b. A motorist is driving too slow.   _____

5. Is it technically correct to say that the speed limit is exactly 55 miles per hour?

   _____

6. Write multiple inequalities for each situation.
   a. The driver's speed is within the speed limits.   _____

   b. The driver's speed is outside of the speed limits.   _____

People use multiple inequalities when they deal with real-estate situations.

7. John and Marsha would like to buy a house priced at $185,000, plus or minus $5,000.
   a. What are the maximum and minimum house price that they are willing to pay?   _____

   b. Write a pair of inequalities describing their price range. _____

8. Use inequalities to describe the following sentence:
   "We sell houses priced at $80,000, plus or minus $5000, to houses priced at $250,000, plus or minus $5000."   _____

Enrichment

6.3 Exploring Patterned Intervals

The inequality $a \leq x \leq b$, where $a < b$, is the set of all real numbers between a and b, including a and b. The corresponding set of points on the number line is called a *closed inverval*.

In Exercises 1–7, n is an integer and $n - \frac{1}{4} \leq x \leq n + \frac{1}{4}$. Graph the solutions for the given values of n on the number line below.

1. $n = 0$

2. $n = 0$ or $n = 1$

3. $n = 0$ or $n = -1$

4. $n = -2, -1, 0, 1,$ or 2

5. $n = -3, -2, -1, 0, 1, 2,$ or 3

6. $n = -4, -3, -2, -1, 0, 1, 2, 3,$ or 4

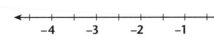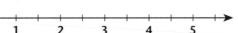

7. Suppose that the graphs for all values of n are shown on the number line. Describe the graph.

_____

For each set of intervals on the given number line, write a compound inequality involving $n, x,$ and conjunction to describe the entire graph.

8. _____

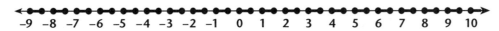

9. _____

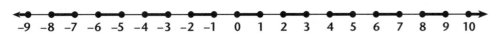

10. _____

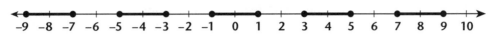

11. a. Let n be an integer. Describe the interval $1 - \frac{1}{n} \leq x \leq 1 + \frac{1}{n}$.

_____

b. What can you say about the interval as n gets larger.

_____

Algebra 1

NAME _____ CLASS _____ DATE _____

Enrichment

6.4 Absolute Value and Distance

You know that the absolute value of a number is its distance from zero. In this worksheet, you will learn other ways in which absolute value is related to distance.

Complete the following exercises.

1. **a.** Graph -3 and 2 on the number line.
   b. What is the distance between -3 and 2? _____
   c. Evaluate $|-3 - 2|$ and $|2 - (-3)|$. Compare your results with your answer to part **b.** _____

   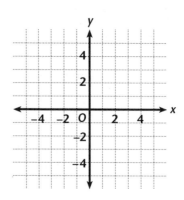

2. **a.** Graph 2 and 4 on the number line.
   b. What is the distance between 2 and 4? _____
   c. Evaluate $|2 - 4|$ and $|4 - 2|$. Compare your results with your answer to part **b.** _____

3. **a.** Graph -3 and -2 on the number line.
   b. What is the distance between -3 and -2? _____
   c. Evaluate $|-3 - (-2)|$ and $|-2 - (-3)|$. Compare your results with your answer to part **b.** _____

4. Based on your results above, how would you describe the quantity $|x - 2|$ in terms of distance?

   _____

5. **a.** Sketch a graph of $y = |x - 2|$.
   b. Give the coordinates for the tip of the V in your graph. _____
   c. Use your answer to Exercise 4 to explain why your answer to part **b** makes sense.

   _____

6. How would you describe the quantity $|x + 3|$, or $|x - (-3)|$, in terms of distance?

   _____

7. **a.** Sketch a graph of $y = |x + 3|$.
   b. Give the coordinates for the tip of the V in your graph. _____
   c. Use your answer to Exercise 6 to explain why your answer to part **b** makes sense.

   _____

Enrichment

6.5 *Using Tolerances in Geometry Problems*

Absolute-value inequalities can be used to describe tolerances. The diagram at right shows a rectangle that is to be used in construction. Its sides should measure x units and y units. Since measurements are rarely exact, the length and width of the rectangle may be slightly less than 12 feet and 9 feet or may be slightly larger than 12 feet and 9 feet, respectively. These variances are shown as the dotted rectangles at right.

For the rectangle at right $|x - 12| \leq 0.5$ and $|y - 9| \leq 0.5$.

In Exercise 1–5, refer to the inequalities above.

1. Solve $|x - 12| \leq 0.5$. _____

2. Solve $|y - 9| \leq 0.5$. _____

3. Using the smallest values of x and y that you found in Exercises 1 and 2, what are the dimensions of the smallest possible rectangle? _____

4. Using the largest values of x and y that you found in Exercises 1 and 2, what are the dimensions of the largest possible rectangle? _____

5. Using the dimensions that you found in Exercises 3 and 4, find

   a. the perimeter of the smallest rectangle.   **b.** the perimeter of the largest rectangle.

   _____   _____

   c. the area of the smallest rectangle.   **d.** the area of the largest rectangle.

   _____   _____

6. **a.** Find the difference between the perimeter of the largest rectangle and the perimeter of the smallest rectangle. _____

   b. Find the difference between the area of the largest rectangle and the area of the smallest rectangle. _____

Now consider a box whose acceptable lengths and widths are determined by the inequalities above and whose acceptable height, z, is determined by $|z - 10| \leq 0.5$.

7. Find the volume of the box with the smallest acceptable dimensions. _____

8. Find the volume of the box with the largest acceptable dimensions. _____

9. By how much does the largest acceptable volume exceed the smallest acceptable volume? _____

Enrichment

7.1 Points of Intersection and Spirals

When you graph the system $\begin{cases} y = \frac{4}{5}x + 4 \\ y = -\frac{1}{2}x + 7 \end{cases}$, you will see a pair

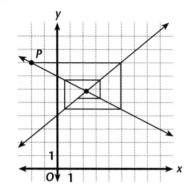

of lines like the ones shown. The point of intersection is clearly visible. From the graph, you can approximate its coordinates.

The diagram also shows point P as well as horizontal and vertical line segments that start from P, link up, and spiral in on the point of intersection.

In Exercises 1–3, graph the equations in each system. Mark the point of intersection and plot point P. Starting from P, draw the first six horizontal and vertical line segments that link up and spiral in on the point of intersection.

1. $\begin{cases} y = 0.5x + 2 \\ y = -x + 4 \end{cases}; P(-2, 1)$

2. $\begin{cases} y = -\frac{1}{2}x + 2 \\ y = x - 2 \end{cases}; P(0, 2)$

3. $\begin{cases} y = x - 1 \\ y = -0.5x - 4 \end{cases}; P(0, -1)$

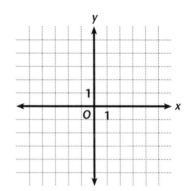

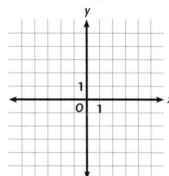

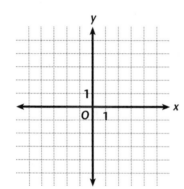

The diagram at right shows the graphs of the equations in the system $\begin{cases} y = \frac{4}{5}x + 4 \\ y = -\frac{1}{2}x + 7 \end{cases}$ and point Q on one of the lines. Refer to this graph in Exercises 4 and 5.

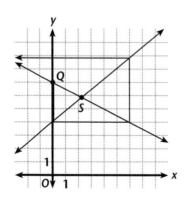

4. Describe what happens when you start from point Q and draw vertical and then horizontal line segments that link up as shown.

_____

5. How do you know that the line segments spiral away from the point of intersection?

_____

Enrichment

7.2 Adapting the Substitution Method

The objective of the substitution method is to transform a pair of linear equations in x and y into a single equation involving only one variable. From that single equation, you find the value of one variable. The value is then used to write a single equation in the other variable. When that equation is solved, the complete solution is found.

In the exercises that follow, you will see that the substitution method can be applied to systems of equations in which no variable has a coefficient of 1.

Complete each of the exercises below.

1. Consider $\begin{cases} 4x + 3y = 7 \\ 4x + 4y = 12 \end{cases}$.

    a. Solve the first equation for $4x$. _____

    b. Replace $4x$ in the second equation with the expression that you wrote for $4x$ in part **a**. Write the resulting equation. _____

    c. Solve the equation that you wrote in part **b** for y. Then find x. _____

Consider $\begin{cases} 6x - 2y + 3 = 0 \\ 2x + 4y - 5 = 0 \end{cases} \rightarrow \begin{cases} 3(2x) - 2y + 3 = 0 \\ 2x + 4y - 5 = 0 \end{cases}$.

2. **a.** Write a single equation in y by solving the second equation for $2x$ and then substituting the equivalent expression into the first equation. Solve for y. _____

    b. Write the solution to the system. _____

3. **a.** Rewrite the given system so that it shows a multiple of y rather than of x. _____

    b. Use substitution to write a single equation in x. Solve for x. Then write the solution to the system. _____

Use a modification of the substitution method to solve each system.

4. $\begin{cases} 16x + 6y - 8 = 0 \\ 4x - 9y + 5 = 0 \end{cases}$ _____

5. $\begin{cases} 3x + 15y - 9 = 0 \\ 4x - 5y + 13 = 0 \end{cases}$ _____

6. $\begin{cases} 3x + ky - 8 = 0 \\ 4x - 2ky + 5 = 0 \end{cases}$ _____

7. $\begin{cases} kx + 3y - 9 = 0 \\ 4kx - 5y + 13 = 0 \end{cases}$ _____

8. Explain how to use the substitution method to solve a system in which the x-term in one equation is a multiple of the x-term in the other equation.

_____

_____

Enrichment

7.3 Automating a Solution Process

Every system of two linear equations in x and y can be written as $\begin{cases} ax + by = e \\ cx + dy = f \end{cases}$.

Since they all have the same form, you may be able to write a formula to solve them.

Consider $\begin{cases} ax + by = e \\ cx + dy = f \end{cases}$.

1. Write the equations in the system $\begin{cases} 5x + 8 = -2y \\ -2 + 3y + 4x = 0 \end{cases}$ in standard form. _____

Consider $\begin{cases} ax + by = e \\ cx + dy = f \end{cases}$.

2. **a.** Write the system of equations that results from multiplying each side of the first equation by d and each side of the second equation by $-b$. _____

   b. Write the sum of the equations in Part a to get a single equation in x. Then solve for x. _____

   c. Write the system of equations that results from multiplying each side of the first equation by c and each side of the second equation by $-a$. _____

   d. Write the sum of the equations in Part c to get a single equation in y. Then solve for y. _____

In Exercise 2, you should find that $x = \dfrac{de - bf}{ad - bc}$ and $y = \dfrac{ce - af}{bc - ad}$.
Use these formulas in Exercises 3–6.

3. $\begin{cases} 3x - 5y = 13 \\ 4x + 3y = 2 \end{cases}$

4. $\begin{cases} 5y = 18 - 2x \\ 3x - 7 = -4y \end{cases}$

_____

_____

5. $\begin{cases} 2x - 3y - 1 = 0 \\ 3x - 4y - 7 = 0 \end{cases}$

6. $\begin{cases} rx - sy = 0 \\ sx + ry = a \end{cases}$, where r, s, and a are nonzero.

_____

_____

7. What can you say about $\begin{cases} ax + by = e \\ cx + dy = f \end{cases}$ if $ad - bc = 0$?

_____

_____

Enrichment

7.4 Using Inconsistent Systems to Advantage

Frequently, when you encounter a system of equations, you are interested in finding a solution. You may be surprised to learn that you can use systems of equations that have no solution to study and create geometric figures. The graph at right represents a system of three equations in two variables, x and y. Since the three lines do not meet in one point, there is no common solution. Notice that the three lines determine a triangle.

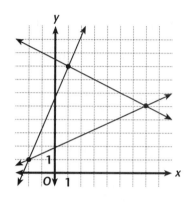

Refer to the graph at right.

1. Write a system of equations in x and y for the three lines shown at right above. Give your equations in slope-intercept form.

_____

2. Write three systems of equations in x and y in order to locate the three vertices of the triangle.

_____

In Exercises 3–5, write a system of equations that describe each figure.

3.

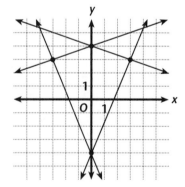

4.

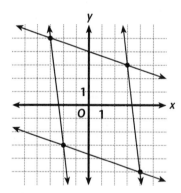

5.

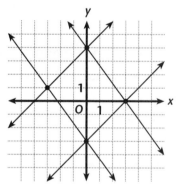

6. In geometry, a *kite* is a four-sided planar figure that has two pairs of adjacent sides of the same length.

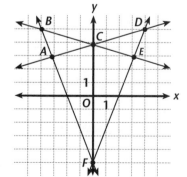

   a. In the graph at right, points F, A, C, and E determine a kite. Represent the kite as a system of equations in x and y. _____

   b. The graph also shows a kite determined by points F, B, C, and D. Represent the kite as a system of equations in x and y. _____

Enrichment

7.5 Systems of Absolute-Value Inequalities

Recall that $|x|$ has two parts in its definition. If $x \geq 0$, then $|x| = x$. If $x < 0$, then $|x| = -x$. This definition is useful when dealing with systems of inequalities that involve absolute value.

In Exercises 1 and 2, consider $\begin{cases} y \geq |x| - 4 \\ y \leq -|x| + 4 \end{cases}$.

1. Consider $y \geq |x| - 4$.

   a. On the grid at right, graph $y = |x| - 4$. Shade the part of the plane that is the solution to $y \geq |x| - 4$. (Test points to help decide on what part of the plane to shade.)

   b. On the grid at right, graph $y = -|x| + 4$. Shade that part of the plane that is the solution to $y \leq -|x| + 4$.

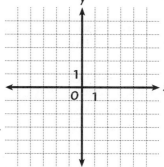

2. Describe the region that is the common solution to the two absolute-value inequalities.

You can reverse the process and represent a specified region by using a system of inequalities.

3. On the grid at right, graph the vertical lines $x = 3$ and $x = -3$. Also graph the horizontal lines $y = 5$ and $y = -5$.

   a. Write a pair of absolute-value inequalities whose graphs are the interior of the rectangle formed.

   _____

   b. Write a pair of absolute-value inequalities whose graphs are the exterior of the rectangle formed.

   _____

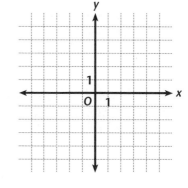

4. Explain how to modify the solution to Exercise 3 in order to represent the rectangle whose sides are bounded by the vertical lines $x = -1$ and $x = 3$ and the horizontal lines $y = 2$ and $y = 8$. Then write the system of absolute-value inequalities.

5. The sides of a square are horizontal and vertical line segments whose diagonals meet at the origin. Represent the square and its interior by using a system of absolute-value inequalities.

Enrichment

7.6 Creating Digit Puzzles from Solutions

The puzzle at right is a digit problem that you can solve by using a system of equations. Did you ever wonder how such puzzles are created?

> The sum of the digits of two two-digit numbers is 7. When the digits are reversed, one number is 3 less than 4 times the other number. What are the numbers?

One way to make up such a puzzle is to start from the answer. Consider the numbers 16 and 61. The sum of their digits is 7. Furthermore, 61 is three less than 4 times the 16.

In Exercises 1–3, write a system of equations for each puzzle. Then solve the puzzle.

1. The sum of the digits of two two-digit numbers is 9. When the digits are reversed, the resulting number is 9 less than 3 times the original number. What are the numbers?

   _____

2. The sum of the digits of two two-digit numbers is 9. When the digits are reversed, the resulting number is 18 more than twice the original number. What are the numbers?

   _____

3. The sum of the digits of two two-digit numbers is 9. When the digits are reversed, the difference of the two numbers is 45. What are the numbers?

   _____

4. The answers to Exercises 1–3 are all the same. Make up a number puzzle different from the ones in Exercises 1–3 but which has the same solution as the puzzles in Exercises 1–3.

   _____

In Exercises 5 and 6, start with the numbers 13 and 31.

5. **a.** Write an equation for the sum of the digits in the numbers. What do your variables represent?

   _____

   b. Write an equation that relates 13 to 31, the number that you get when you reverse the digits. _____

   c. Write another equation that relates 13 and 31. _____

Enrichment
8.1 *Exploring Patterns in the Units Digit of x^n*

When you write out the first several powers of x^n, where x and n are positive integers, you can discover interesting patterns in the units digits in x^n.

	x^1	x^2	x^3	x^4	x^5	x^6
$x = 2$	$2^1 = 2$	$2^2 = 2(2) = 4$	$2^3 = 2(4) = 8$	$2^4 = 2(8) = 16$	$2^5 = 2(16) = 32$	$2^6 = 2(32) = 64$

Notice that 2^1 and 2^5 have the same units digit and that 2^2 and 2^6 have the same units digit. In the exercises that follow, you can discover other number patterns involving the units digits of x^n.

In Exercises 1–10, find the first nine powers of each value of x. Using the units digit of each result, complete the table. You may find a calculator useful.

		x^1	x^2	x^3	x^4	x^5	x^6	x^7	x^8	x^9
1.	$x = 1$									
2.	$x = 2$									
3.	$x = 3$									
4.	$x = 4$									
5.	$x = 5$									
6.	$x = 6$									
7.	$x = 7$									
8.	$x = 8$									
9.	$x = 9$									
10.	$x = 10$									

Refer to the table that you completed in Exercises 1–10. Describe the pattern in the units digits of x^n.

11. 1^n _____

12. 2^n _____

13. 3^n _____

14. 5^n _____

15. Write a rule that determines the units digit of 7^n as a function of n.

_____

Enrichment

8.2 Even and Odd Powers

Suppose that you consider a positive number b and positive integer exponents n. Because of the logic shown at right, you can see that the powers of $-b$ alternate between negative and positive values.

$(-b)^n = (-1 \times b)^n = (-1)^n b^n$

In Exercises 1–4, n is a positive integer and P_n has coordinates $\left((-2)^n, (-2)^{n-1}\right)$.

1. Complete the table below.

n	$x = (-2)^n$	$y = (-2)^{n-1}$	(x, y)
1	-2	1	$(-2, 1)$
2			
3			
4			
5			
6			
7			

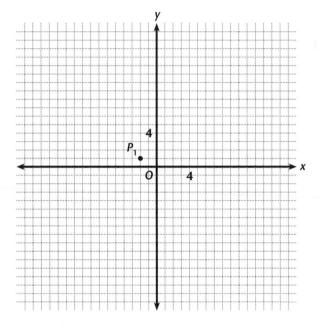

2. Plot the points P_2, P_3, and P_4 for $n = 2, 3$, and 4 on the grid above. Point P_1, corresponding to $n = 1$, is already plotted for you.

3. Find the slopes of $\overline{P_1 P_2}$, $\overline{P_2 P_3}$, and $\overline{P_1 P_3}$.

4. Make a conjecture about the set of points P_n that you would get if you let $n = 1, 2, 3, 4, \ldots$

In Exercises 5–7, P_n has coordinates as given. Make a conjecture about the set of points that you would get if you let $n = 1, 2, 3, 4, \ldots$ You will need to know that 2^0, $(-3)^0$, and 3^0 equal 1.

5. $P_n(2^n, 2^{n-1})$ _____

6. $P_n((-3)^n, (-3)^{n-1})$ _____

7. $P_n(3^n, 3^{n-1})$ _____

8. Suppose that you let P_n have coordinates $\left((-2)^{2n}, (-2)^{2n-1}\right)$. What can you say about the set of points that is created when various values are substituted for n?

_____

Enrichment

8.3 *Using Exponents to Understand Multiplication of Decimals*

When you learned how to multiply one decimal by another, you learned to count decimal places and move the decimal point that many places to the left.

$0.003 \times 0.02 \longrightarrow$ Write 6 and move the decimal point 5 places to the left. $\longrightarrow 0.00006$

Using properties of exponents, you can understand why this rule works.

Find each product by counting decimal places and moving the decimal point.

1. 0.06×0.002 _____

2. 0.04×0.012 _____

3. 0.15×0.0006 _____

4. 0.09×0.00012 _____

You can also find the product 0.003×0.02 by using a property of exponents that you learned. Notice that the final answer shown below agrees with the answer obtained by applying the rule for multiplication shown in the example above.

$$0.003 \times 0.02 = \frac{3}{1000} \times \frac{2}{100} = \frac{3}{10^3} \times \frac{2}{10^2} = \frac{3 \times 2}{10^3 \times 10^2} = \frac{3 \times 2}{10^{3+2}} = \frac{6}{10^5} = \frac{6}{10,000} = 0.00006$$

Find each product by using a property of exponents as shown above. Show your work.

5. 0.06×0.002 _____

6. 0.04×0.012 _____

7. 0.15×0.0006 _____

8. 0.09×0.00012 _____

John and Martha wondered if they could write a rule by which they could easily find the product of three decimals between 0 and 1.

Find each product by using a property of exponents. Show your work.

9. $0.06 \times 0.002 \times 0.003$ _____

10. $0.04 \times 0.05 \times 0.003$ _____

11. Write an extension of the rule for multiplying two decimals between 0 and 1 that applies to multiplying three such decimals.

_____

Algebra 1

Enrichment

8.4 Applying Properties of Exponents to Rational Numbers

You can use the following three facts to discover a new and interesting fact about rational numbers:

- A rational number is the quotient of two integers with a nonzero denominator.
- Every integer can be written as a product of powers of prime numbers, called the *prime factorization* of the given number. For example, $120 = 2^3 3^1 5^1$.
- When dividing two powers with the same base, subtract the exponents.
  $\frac{10^5}{10^3} = 10^2$ and $\frac{10^3}{10^5} = \frac{1}{10^2}$

Write the prime factorization of each integer.

1. 24 _____

2. 108 _____

3. 452 _____

4. 1800 _____

For each rational number, write the numerator and denominator by using the prime factorization of each. Then use the Quotient-of-Powers Property to simplify the result. Do not multiply out the powers of prime numbers that remain.

5. $\frac{18}{24}$ _____

6. $\frac{48}{180}$ _____

7. $\frac{250}{288}$ _____

8. $\frac{540}{1800}$ _____

9. Examine the final quotients that you wrote in Exercises 5–8. Explain why a prime-number base that appears in a numerator does not appear in the denominator and why a prime-number base that appears in a denominator does not appear in the numerator.

_____

_____

10. Let $\frac{a}{b}$ be a rational number. Write a generalization about the representation of $\frac{a}{b}$ as the quotient of prime numbers raised to powers. Illustrate your generalization by using $\frac{54}{120} = \frac{2^1 3^3}{2^3 3^1 5^1}$.

_____

_____

Enrichment

8.5 Using Scientific Notation to Make Comparisons

The average distance between Earth and the sun is 93,000,000 miles. The average distance between Jupiter and the sun is 484,000,000 miles. Using scientific notation, you can answer questions like the one below.

How many times farther from the sun is Jupiter than Earth?

Answer the following questions.

1. **a.** Write the distance between Earth and the sun in scientific notation.

    _____

    b. Write the distance between Jupiter and the sun in scientific notation.

    _____

    c. Write the ratio,
    $$\frac{\text{distance between Jupiter and the sun}}{\text{distance between Earth and the sun}},$$
    in scientific notation.

    _____

2. The average distance between Pluto and the sun is 3,675,000,000 miles.

    a. How many times farther from the sun is Pluto than Earth?

    _____

    b. How many times farther from the sun is Pluto than Jupiter?

    _____

3. The star closest to the sun is 25,000,000,000,000 miles from the sun. How many times farther is it from the sun to the nearest star as it is from Earth to the sun? _____

One light-year is the distance light travels in one year. Light travels 186,282 miles in 1 second.

4. How many miles does light travel in a year? Give your answer in scientific notation rounded to the nearest tenth.

5. **a.** One galaxy is 200,000 light-years from the sun. How many miles from the sun is the galaxy?

    _____

    b. How many times farther is this galaxy from the sun than Earth is from the sun?

    _____

You can use scientifc notation to compare masses of large objects with masses of small objects.

Mass of hydrogen atom:	1.67×10^{-24} grams
Jerry's mass:	6.35×10^{1} kilograms
Mass of Earth:	5.97×10^{24} kilograms

6. Write a ratio to compare Jerry's mass with that of a hydrogen atom. _____

7. Write a ratio to compare the mass of Earth with that of a hydrogen atom. _____

Enrichment

8.6 Exploring Reciprocals and Reflections

The diagram at right shows a triangle and its reflection across the y-axis. Notice that the triangle and its reflection are congruent figures.

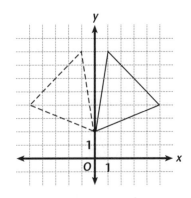

Graph each pair of functions on the grid provided. Describe how the bases of the exponential functions are related. Then describe how each graph is related to the other.

1. $y = 2^x$ and $y = \left(\frac{1}{2}\right)^x$

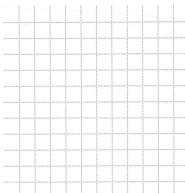

2. $y = 3^x$ and $y = \left(\frac{1}{3}\right)^x$

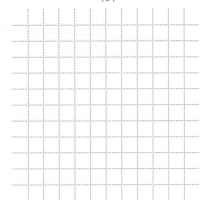

3. Let b be a number greater than 1. Consider $y = b^x$ and $y = \left(\frac{1}{b}\right)^x$. Write a statement that describes how the bases are related and how the graphs are related.

_____

Without sketching any graphs, state how the graphs in each pair are related. Justify your response.

4. $y = 10^x$ and $y = \left(\frac{1}{10}\right)^x$

5. $y = 5^x$ and $y = 0.2^x$

_____   _____

6. $y = 4^x$ and $y = 4^{-x}$

7. $y = \left(\frac{5}{4}\right)^x$ and $y = 1.25^{-x}$

_____   _____

Enrichment

8.7 *Planning to Make Donations*

Some of the parents of the students in a mathematics class invest money in accounts that pay compound interest. Their hope is to have their investments grow so that, at some time in the future, they can use the money that has accumulated to help the local Boys and Girls Club. The compound interest that they need for their financial planning is shown at right.

$$A = P(1 + r)^t \begin{cases} P \text{ represents the initial amount} \\ r \text{ represents the rate as a decimal} \\ t \text{ represents time in years} \\ A \text{ represents the final amount} \end{cases}$$

Suppose that $10,000 is invested into an account that pays 5.65% interest compounded annually. Give answers rounded to the nearest cent.

1. Write a function that will give A as a function of t. _____

2. Complete the table below.

t	0	1	2	3	4	5	6	7
A								

3. **a.** After how many years will their initial
        deposit exceed $12,000?   _____

    b. After how many years will their initial
        deposit exceed $12,000 but be less than $14,000? _____

4. The group of parents want their initial deposit amount to grow to $15,000. Use guess-and-check to approximate the number of years that it will take for this to happen. Give your answer to the nearest tenth of a year. _____

5. The group wants their initial deposit amount to grow to $18,000 within 10 years. After that time, they want to make an $18,000 donation to the local club.
    a. Will they achieve their goal? Explain your response.

        _____

    b. By how much will they exceed or fall short of their goal?   _____

Use guess-and-check to approximate the time that it takes the given investment to grow to the target goal. Round answers to the nearest tenth of a year.

6. $12,500 at 4.5% compounded yearly; target goal: $18,000 _____

7. $15,500 at 6.5% compounded yearly; target goal: $20,000 _____

8. $5 at 5.5% compounded yearly; target goal: $18,000   _____

9. $5 at 1% compounded yearly; target goal: $200,000   _____

Enrichment

9.1 Understanding Carrying in Addition

In your earlier training in mathematics, you learned how to add two whole numbers and *carry* when necessary. To understand the reasoning behind carrying, you need to write whole numbers in expanded form. The expanded form of 36 is $36 = 3 \times 10 + 6$

$$
\begin{array}{rl}
36 \longrightarrow & 3 \times 10 + 6 \\
+\ 28 \longrightarrow & +\ 2 \times 10 + 8 \\
\hline
& (3 + 2) \times 10 + 14 = (3 + 2) \times 10 + \mathbf{1} \times 10 + 4 \\
& = (3 + 2 + \mathbf{1}) \times 10 + 4 \qquad \text{Distributive Property} \\
& = 6 \times 10 + 4 \\
& = 64
\end{array}
$$

In Exercises 1 and 2, add by using expanded form and the pattern above. Show your work.

1. $56 + 37$ 　　　　　　　　　　　　**2.** $67 + 15$

3. Under what conditions, placed on the units digit of two numbers, would you

　a. not carry from the units place to the tens place? _____

　b. carry from the units place to the tens place? _____

4. Sometimes you carry 1 from the units place to the tens place. Do you ever carry 2 or more? Why or why not? _____

_____

The sum of two two-digit numbers might be a three-digit number. In such problems, you need to create a place for 100, or 10^2, in the answer.

Use the process shown at the top of the page to perform the following addition problems. Show your work.

5. $78 + 67$ 　　　　　　　　　　　　**6.** $87 + 79$

7. Write two three-digit numbers whose sum requires carrying from every place to the next place to the left. Verify by using the process shown at the top of the page.

Enrichment

9.2 Patterns in Special Products

The expansions of $(a + b)^2$, $(a - b)^2$, and $(a + b)(a - b)$ show patterns involving a and b. You can discover other patterns involving a and b when you combine these special products.

In Exercises 1–5, use the given values of a and b to complete the table below.

	a	b	$(a + b)^2$	$(a - b)^2$	$(a + b)^2 - (a - b)^2$	ab
1.	-3	5				
2.	-2	-4				
3.	3	6				
4.	4	7				
5.	5	-8				

6. a. From the table, how are the values of $(a + b)^2 - (a - b)^2$ and ab related?

_____

  b. Based on your work in Exercises 1–5 and your answer
    to part **a**, write a simplification of $(a + b)^2 - (a + b)^2$. _____

  c. Use algebra to show that your response to part **b** is true.

_____

7. Using a table like the one that you completed in Exercises 1–5
    and the values of a and b used there, write a simplification
    of $(a + b)^2 + (a - b)^2$.   _____

Write a conjecture for the simplification of each sum or difference. Try to do as much of the simplification as you can mentally.

8. $[(a^2 + b^2) + (a^2 - b^2)]^2$

9. $[(a^2 + b^2) - (a^2 - b^2)]^2$

_____   _____

Simplify each expression.

10. $[(a^2 + b^2) + (a^2 - b^2)]^2$

11. $[(a^2 + b^2) - (a^2 - b^2)]^2$

_____   _____

Enrichment
9.3 Understanding a Multiplication Procedure

In your earlier training in mathematics, you learned a method for multiplying whole numbers. According to that method, you use addition along with multiplication.

$$\begin{array}{r} 31 \\ \times\ 23 \\ \hline 93 \\ +\ 62 \\ \hline 713 \end{array}$$

The multiplication problem shown at right is worked out in great detail below by using expanded form and the Distributive Property. Notice that, as you might expect, the results are the same.

$$31 \times 23 \longrightarrow \begin{array}{r} 3 \times 10 + 1 \\ \times\ 2 \times 10 + 3 \\ \hline 9 \times 10 + 3 \end{array}$$

$$\begin{array}{r} +\ 6 \times 100 +\ \ 2 \times 10 \\ \hline 6 \times 100 + 11 \times 10 + 3 \end{array}$$

Simplify the sum.

$6 \times 100 + (\mathbf{10} + \mathbf{1})(10) + 3$
$6 \times 100 + 100 + 10 + 3$
$6 \times 100 + 1 \times 100 + 1 \times 10 + 3$
$(6 + 1) \times 100 + (1 \times 10) + 3$
713

In Exercises 1 and 2, find each product by using the method that you learned in earlier grades and the method shown above. Show your work in the space provided.

1. $\begin{array}{r} 13 \\ \times\ 22 \end{array}$

2. $\begin{array}{r} 13 \\ \times\ 16 \end{array}$

3. You can represent a two-digit number whose units digit is 1 as $10t + 1$, where t represents the tens digit. The variable t can be an integer from 1 to 9 inclusive. Complete the multiplication shown at right. Under what conditions, placed on t and r, will the product be more than 1000?

$$\begin{array}{r} 10t + 1 \\ \times\ 10r + 1 \end{array}$$

Enrichment

9.4 *Exploring Families of Functions and Graphs*

If you let n be a positive integer greater than 1, then functions of the form $y = x^n$ make up a family of functions. Members of this family separate into two different sets of functions, as you will see.

In Exercises 1–4, complete each table of values for the given function. Then make a rough sketch of the graph on the axes provided. Your sketch should show the general trend.

1. $y = x^2$

x	y
−3	
−2	
−1	
0	
1	
2	
3	

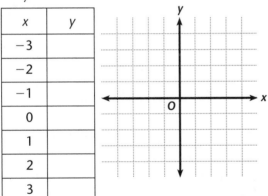

2. $y = x^4$

x	y
−3	
−2	
−1	
0	
1	
2	
3	

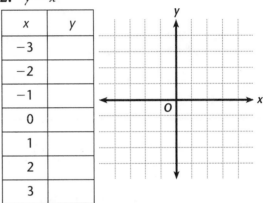

3. $y = x^3$

x	y
−3	
−2	
−1	
0	
1	
2	
3	

4. $y = x^5$

x	y
−3	
−2	
−1	
0	
1	
2	
3	

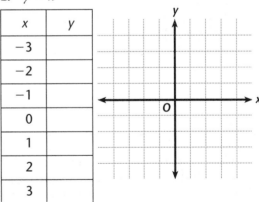

5. Based on your work in Exercises 1–4, describe the shape of $y = x^6$ and $y = x^8$.

_____

6. Based on your work in Exercises 1–4, describe the shape of $y = x^7$ and $y = x^9$.

_____

7. Let n be an integer greater than 1. Explain how you know that the graph of $y = x^n$ is U-shaped when n is even and S-shaped when n is odd.

_____

_____

Enrichment
9.5 Using Prime Factorization to Find the GCF

There are many reasons why you might need to factor a number. Small numbers are easily factorable, and you can write their factors with a small amount of work. For large numbers, such as 180, you can use the method shown at right. Notice that the method is based on successive division by small prime numbers. First try 2 as a divisor, then try 3, and so on. From the division shown at right, you can write the prime factorization of 180 as follows.

$$2 \overline{)180}$$
$$2 \overline{)90}$$
$$3 \overline{)45}$$
$$3 \overline{)15}$$
$$5 \overline{)5}$$
$$1$$

$$180 = 2 \times 2 \times 3 \times 3 \times 5 = 2^2 3^2 5$$

Using the method shown at right above, find the prime factorization of each number.

1. 825   2. 1575   3. 1024   4. 25,200

_____   _____   _____   _____

Once you have written two large numbers by using their prime factorization, you can easily find their common factors.

List the distinct prime-number factors of each pair of numbers. If the numbers have no common factors other than 1, write *relatively prime*.

5. $2^2 3^2 5^2 7^2$ and $2^1 3^3 5^9 7^4$ 6. $2^5 3^2 11^2 13^5$ and $2^1 11^3 19^9$

_____   _____

7. $2^{10} 5^8 23^2 53^2$ and $3^{17} 3^{17} 9^{19} 4$ 8. $5^5 3^2 17^2 31^5$ and $2^1 11^3 5^5 3^2 17^2 31^5$

_____   _____

Once you have identified which prime numbers are common factors of two numbers, then find the highest powers of those prime factors that are common factors. The product of such powers gives the greatest common factor (GCF) of the two numbers.

Find the greatest common factor of each pair of numbers.

9. the pair in Exercise 5   10. the pair in Exercise 6

_____   _____

11. the pair in Exercise 7   12. the pair in Exercise 8

_____   _____

13. 3,293,136 and 3,778,488   14. 2,662,000 and 26,159,679

_____   _____

Enrichment

9.6 *Exploring $a^n - b^n$ and $a^n + b^n$*

You already know the facts stated below.

$a^2 - b^2 = (a + b)(a - b)$ and $a^2 + b^2$ cannot be factored by using real numbers.

In the exercises that follow, you will be able to study the factorability of differences and sums involving exponents greater than or equal to 2.

In Exercises 1 and 2, consider $a^n - b^n$ for $n = 3$ and $n = 4$, respectively.

1. Show that $a^3 - b^3 = (a - b)(a^2 + ab + b^2)$ by performing the multiplication started at right. Show your work in the space provided.

$$\begin{array}{r} a^2 + ab + b^2 \\ \times \qquad a - b \\ \hline \end{array}$$

2. Show that $a^4 - b^4 = (a + b)(a - b)(a^2 + b^2)$ by following the reasoning started at right. Notice that the difference of fourth powers is written as a new difference of squares.

$$a^4 - b^4 = (a^2)^2 - (b^2)^2$$
$$= \left(\Box + \Box\right)\left(\Box - \Box\right)$$

In Exercises 3 and 4, consider $a^n + b^n$ for $n = 3$ and $n = 2$, respectively.

3. Show that $a^3 + b^3 = (a + b)(a^2 - ab + b^2)$ by performing the multiplication started at right. Show your work in the space provided.

$$\begin{array}{r} a^2 - ab + b^2 \\ \times \qquad a + b \\ \hline \end{array}$$

4. Suppose that $a^2 + b^2$ can be factored as $a^2 + b^2 = (ra + sb)(ta + bu)$, where r, s, t, and u are numbers and a and b are variables. The reasoning shown at right will help you see that $a^2 + b^2$ cannot be factored.

$$\begin{aligned} a^2 + b^2 &= (ra + sb)(ta + bu) \\ &= (rt)a^2 + (st + ru)ab + (su)b^2 \end{aligned}$$
So, $1 = rt$, $0 = st + ru$, and $1 = su$
$$r = \frac{1}{t}, \ -st = ru, \text{ and } s = \frac{1}{u}$$
Thus, $-\dfrac{t}{u} = \dfrac{u}{t}$
$$-t^2 = u^2$$
$$t = 0 \text{ and } u = 0$$

    a. How do you know that $1 = rt$, $0 = st + ru$, and $1 = su$?

_____

    b. Explain how $t = 0$ and $u = 0$ tell you that there are no values of r and s that make the factorization possible.

_____

_____

Enrichment

9.7 Pushing Back the Boundaries of Factoring

One day, Denise's mathematics teacher, Ms. Dolenze, asked her to factor $6x^2 + 5x + 1$. After puzzling over the problem for a while, Denise told Ms. Dolenze that the expression could not be factored. Amazed, Ms. Dolenze asked Denise why. "I could not find two binomials in x with integer coefficients whose product is $6x^2 + 5x + 1$," replied Denise. Then Ms. Dolenze quickly responded, "Why should that stop you?"

In the exercises that follow, you will see how to push back the boundaries of factoring.

In Exercise 1–4, answer each question in order to help Denise factor $6x^2 + 5x + 1$.

1. By what property of real numbers, can you justify $6x^2 + 5x + 1 = 6\left(x^2 + \frac{5}{6}x + \frac{1}{6}\right)$? _____

2. Show that $\left(\frac{1}{2}\right)\left(\frac{1}{3}\right) = \frac{1}{6}$ and that $\frac{1}{2} + \frac{1}{3} = \frac{5}{6}$.

_____

3. Show that $6\left(x + \frac{1}{2}\right)\left(x + \frac{1}{3}\right) = 6x^2 + 5x + 1$.

_____

4. Is the product in Exercise 3 a factorization of $6x^2 + 5x + 1$? Is it necessary to find integers in order to factor a quadratic trinomial? Explain your response.

_____

Factor each quadratic trinomial as a number times a product of two linear binomials in x, each having rational numbers among the coefficients. Use Exercises 1–3 above as a model.

5. $15x^2 + 8x + 1$ 6. $28x^2 + 11x + 1$

_____   _____

7. $6x^2 - 23x + 20$ 8. $12x^2 + x - 35$

_____   _____

On another occasion, Ms. Dolenze asked Denise if $x^2 + x + 1$ could be factored. This time, Denise proclaimed that the expression could not be factored even by using rational numbers for coefficients. She is correct.

9. Write an argument that helps show that Denise is correct.

_____

_____

Enrichment

9.8 Exploring Rational Roots of Quadratic Equations

In Lesson 8.8, you learned how to use factoring to solve a quadratic equation. The process can be applied to many quadratic equations whose square terms have coefficients other than 1. Consider $10x^2 + 7x - 12 = 0$. At right, you can see how to use factoring and the Zero-Product Property to solve the equation. Notice that the roots of the given equation are rational numbers, not integers.

$$10x^2 + 7x - 12 = 0$$
$$(2x + 3)(5x - 4) = 0$$
$$2x + 3 = 0 \text{ or } 5x - 4 = 0$$
$$x = -\frac{3}{2} \text{ or } x = \frac{4}{5}$$

In Exercises 1–4, factor each quadratic expression by filling in each box with an integer. Use trial and error to find the correct integers. Then use the Zero-Product Property to find the roots.

1. $6x^2 + x - 1$

   $= \left(\square x + \square\right)\left(\square x + \square\right)$

   _____

2. $5x^2 - 13x - 6$

   $= \left(\square x + \square\right)\left(\square x + \square\right)$

   _____

3. $6x^2 - 23x + 20$

   $= \left(\square x + \square\right)\left(\square x + \square\right)$

   _____

4. $12x^2 + x - 35$

   $= \left(\square x + \square\right)\left(\square x + \square\right)$

   _____

Consider the quadratic expression $ax^2 + bx + c$ and its factorization below.

$$ax^2 + bx + c \longrightarrow (rx + s)(tx + u),$$

where r, s, t, and u are integers and x is the variable. The reasoning shown at right indicates how the numbers in the factorization are related to the roots. The equation $ax^2 + bx + c = (rt)x^2 + (ru + st)x + su$ also shows that $a = rt$ and that $c = su$.

$$ax^2 + bx + c = 0$$
$$(rx + s)(tx + u) = 0$$
$$x = -\frac{s}{r} \text{ or } x = -\frac{u}{t}$$

5. The equation $a = rt$ shows that r and t are factors of a, the coefficient of x^2. What does the equation $c = su$ show? _____

6. The equations $x = -\frac{s}{r}$ and $x = -\frac{u}{t}$ along with your answer to Exercise 5 show that the denominator of a root is a factor of a. What do the equations $x = -\frac{s}{r}$ and $x = -\frac{u}{t}$ and your answer to Exercise 5 tell you about the numerator of a root and c?

   _____

7. Maxine argued that when a quadratic equation has rational roots, the denominators are factors of the coefficient of x^2, and the numerators are factors of the constant term c. Use your response to Exercise 6 and the equation $6x^2 - 23x + 20 = 0$ to confirm or deny her claim.

   _____

Enrichment

10.1 The Axis of Symmetry for a Parabola

You can find an equation for the axis of symmetry of a parabola by using the coefficients of an equation in the form $y = ax^2 + bx + c$.

Let $y = 2x^2 - 8x + 11$. In Exercises 1–4, refer to the graph shown at right.

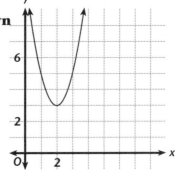

1. Complete each table of values below.

x	-1	0	1	2	3	4	5
y							

x	1.7	1.8	1.9	2.0	2.1	2.2	2.3
y							

2. Write the coordinates of the vertex of the parabola.   _____

3. Using your conclusions from Exercises 1 and 2, write an equation for the axis of symmetry.   _____

4. Find the value of $\dfrac{-b}{2a}$ in $y = 2x^2 - 8x + 11$.   _____

Let $y = -3x^2 - 6x - 5$.

5. Complete the table of values below.

x	-1.3	-1.2	-1.1	-1.0	-0.9	-0.8	-0.7
y							

6. Write the coordinates of the vertex of the parabola.   _____

7. Using the table in Exercise 5, write an equation for the axis of symmetry.   _____

8. Find the value of $\dfrac{-b}{2a}$ in $y = -3x^2 - 6x - 5$.   _____

Let $y = ax^2 + bx + c$.

9. a. Write a conjecture that gives an equation for the axis of symmetry of the parabola in terms of the coefficients of $y = ax^2 + bx + c$.

_____

b. Explain how to verify the conjecture that you wrote in part **a**.

_____

Enrichment
10.2 Irrational Square Roots

You know that $\sqrt{9} = 3$ because if 3 is squared, the result is 9.
In other words, $3^2 = 9$.

This is helpful as long as you take the square root of a number that is a perfect square.

perfect squares: 0, 1, 4, 9, 16, 25, 36, 49, . . .

But what does something like $\sqrt{12}$ mean?

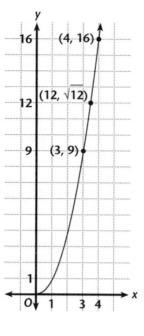

1. The graph of $y = x^2$, shown at right, indicates that when $y = 12$, x is between which two integers? _____

After you find two consecutive integers between which a square root lies, you can use a method called *divide and average* to find a better approximation for that square root.

2. **a.** The average of 3 and 4 is 3.5. Evaluate 3.5^2. _____

    b. How does 3.5 compare to $\sqrt{12}$? _____

    c. Part **b** indicates that $\sqrt{12}$ must be some number between 3 and what number? _____

    d. What is $12 \div 3.5$? _____

    e. Average 3.5 and your answer to part **d**. _____

3. For how many places past the decimal does your answer to part **e** of Exercise 2 match the calculator value for $\sqrt{12}$. _____

Using the procedure outlined in Exercise 2, approximate each square root to the nearest tenth.

4. $\sqrt{13}$

5. $\sqrt{20}$

6. If you use this process on a number that is not a perfect square, will you ever get an exact answer? Explain your response.

_____

Enrichment

10.3 Using Coordinates of the Vertex to Explore x-Intercepts

To write $y = x^2 - 7x + 3$ in the form $y = (x - h)^2 + k$, you could follow these steps.

$$y = x^2 - 7x + 3$$

$$y = x^2 - 7x + \left(\frac{-7}{2}\right)^2 + 3 - \left(\frac{-7}{2}\right)^2$$

$$y = \left(x - \frac{7}{2}\right)^2 + 3 - \frac{7^2}{4}$$

Notice that the number outside the parentheses has not been simplified; leaving it in this form will help you to see a pattern in the following exercises.

Use the method shown above to rewrite each function in the form $y = (x - h)^2 + k$.

1. $y = x^2 + 5x - 1$ **2.** $y = x^2 - 11x + 6$ **3.** $y = x^2 + bx + c$

4. Recall that the vertex of the graph of $y = (x - h)^2 + k$ is at (h, k). Use your answer to Exercise 3 to give the coordinates of the vertex of the graph of $y = x^2 + bx + c$ in terms of b and c.

For Exercises 5–7, consider the parabola whose equation is $y = ax^2 + bx + c$.

5. How do you know that the graph of this parabola opens upward? _____

6. How does the y-coordinate of the vertex show whether the parabola crosses the x-axis?

7. How many x-intercepts does the graph of $y = x^2 + bx + c$ have if you know that

    a. $c - \dfrac{b^2}{4} > 0$? _____

    b. $c - \dfrac{b^2}{4} = 0$? _____

    c. $c - \dfrac{b^2}{4} < 0$? _____

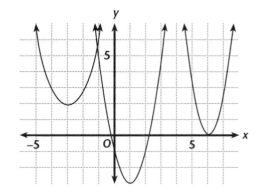

Use your answers to Exercises 4 and 7 to determine (a) the coordinates of the vertex and (b) the number of x-intercepts for each of the following functions.

8. $y = x^2 + 2x - 8$ **9.** $y = x^2 - 9x + 18$

    a. _____ **a.** _____

    b. _____ **b.** _____

Enrichment

10.4 The Intermediate Value Theorem

The Intermediate Value Theorem is a topic that is usually covered in a calculus course. However, you can begin to understand this concept by completing the following set of exercises:

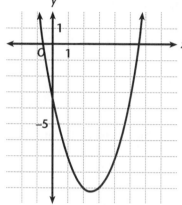

1. The graph for the function $y = x^2 - 5x - 3$ is shown at right. What happens to the graph of this parabola between the x-values of 5 and 6?

    _____

2. Complete the following table for this function:

x	5.3	5.4	5.5	5.6	5.7	5.8	5.9
y							

3. **a.** For which x-coordinates in this table is the y-coordinate positive? _____

    b. For which x-coordinates in this table is the y-coordinate negative? _____

4. How do your answers to Exercise 3 confirm your answer to Exercise 1?

    _____

5. Is there a value of x between 5.5 and 5.6 for which the y-coordinate is 0?

6. By substituting several decimal values for x into $y = x^2 - 5x - 3$, find an approximate zero for this function. _____

The graph of a parabola is said to be a *continuous* curve. This means that the graph has no gaps or breaks in it. For a continuous curve, the Intermediate Value Theorem guarantees that between a point on the curve with a positive y-coordinate and another point with a negative y-coordinate, there must be at least one point on the graph whose y-coordinate equals 0; that is, there is at least one zero of the function.

7. Re-examine the graph above. Find an approximate value for another zero of $y = x^2 - 5x - 3$. _____

8. Without using a graph, use the following table to help you locate two zeros for the function $y = 6x^2 + 5x - 6$. _____

x	-3	-2	-1	0	1	2	3
y							

Enrichment

10.5 Solving Quadratic Equations

The general form of a quadratic equation is $ax^2 + bx + c = 0$, where $a \neq 0$.

Identify a, b, and c for each of the following quadratic equations.

1. $2x^2 - 5x - 8 = 0$ **2.** $7x^2 - 56 = 0$ **3.** $12x^2 - 16x = 0$

_____   _____   _____

4. Why is $5x - 15 = 0$ not a quadratic equation? _____

Three methods for solving quadratic equations are taking square roots, factoring, and using the quadratic formula. Although the quadratic formula can be used to solve any quadratic equation, often one of the other methods is more efficient.

Use Exercises 1–3 to answer the following questions:

5. For which exercise would *taking square roots* be the quickest way to find a solution?   _____

6. For which exercise would *factoring* be the quickest way to find a solution?   _____

7. For which exercise would *using the quadratic formula* be the quickest way to find a solution?   _____

Complete the following table to help you organize the results from the above exercises:

		Example	Method
	If $b = 0$ and $c = 0$	$5x^2 = 0$	none; $x = 0$
8.	If $b = 0$ and $c \neq 0$		
9.	If $b \neq 0$ and $c = 0$		
10.	If $b \neq 0$ and $c \neq 0$		

11. Solve $ax^2 = 0$ for x. _____

12. Solve $ax^2 - c = 0$ for x in terms of a and c. _____

13. Solve $ax^2 + bx = 0$ for x in terms of a and b. _____

14. Solve $ax^2 + bx + c = 0$ for x in terms of a, b and c. _____

15. What is the name of the formula you found in Exercise 14? _____

Enrichment

10.6 Creating Graphs With Personality

The shading in the graph at right shows the intersection of
$y \le 0.25x^2 + 1$ and $y \ge x^2$.

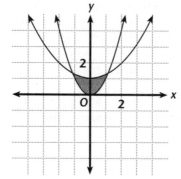

1. What is the mathematical term for the
   shape of each of the curves in this graph? _____

2. Describe how the two curves in this graph differ from each other.

   _____

To determine which inequality represents which parabola, notice the
vertex of each.

3. Write the inequality for the parabola that has
   part of its graph below the shaded region. _____

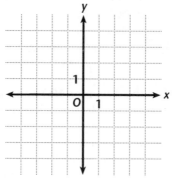

4. Use your calculator to help you sketch the region that is the
   intersection of $y \le 0.6x^2 + 1$ and $y \ge x^2$. Use the grid at the right.

5. How does this shaded region differ from the one at the top of
   the page?

   _____

Use your graphics calculator to experiment with different values for a in
$y \le ax^2 + 1$ while keeping the other inequality as $y \ge x^2$.

You may have noticed that the shaded region has the same shape as a
smile. What happens to the "smile," if

6. $a > 1$? _____

7. $0 < a < 1$? _____

8. $a < 0$? _____

Notice how a negative value of a, as in Exercise 8, changes the direction of
the parabola. Use the inequality $y \ge x^2$ to complete Exercise 9. Notice the
change in the inequality sign.

9. See if you can create a "frown" by using the above inequality and
   another region that is some alteration of $y \ge x^2$. Describe your
   inequality and your results.

   _____

   _____

Enrichment
11.1 Seesaws

When two children of different weights sit on a seesaw that is joined to the pivot at its midpoint, one child sits higher than the pivot point, and the other child sits lower than it. They achieve balance and reverse who is higher and who is lower by exerting a downward force on the ground.

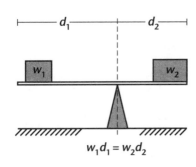

$$w_1 d_1 = w_2 d_2$$

The diagram at right shows two different weights positioned at different distances from the pivot point of a seesaw. The equation indicates that weight and distance have an inverse variation. w_1 and w_2 represent weight, and d_1 and d_2 represent distance.

In Exercises 1–3, the total length of a seesaw is 12 feet, and boxes A and B are balanced.

1. Boxes A and B weigh 60 pounds and 80 pounds, respectively. How far from the pivot point is box A if box B is 4 feet from the pivot point ?

   _____

2. Box A weighs 100 pounds and is 5 feet from the pivot point of the seesaw. How much does box B weigh if it is 6 feet from the pivot point?

   _____

3. Boxes A and B weigh 120 pounds and 150 pounds, respectively. How far is each box from the pivot point of the seesaw? (Hint: Let x represent the distance between box A and the pivot point. Then write and solve an equation for x.)

   _____

In Exercises 4 and 5, solve each seesaw problem. The length of the board used to balance boxes A and B is 20 feet.

4. Boxes A and B weigh 60 pounds and 80 pounds, respectively. John wants to put box A at the left end of the board and to position the pivot point 5 feet to the right of box A. How far from the right end of the board should he place box B?

   _____

5. Boxes A and B weigh 60 pounds and 80 pounds, respectively. John wants to put box A at the left end of the board and to position the pivot point 15 feet to the right of box A. Is it possible to put box B on the seesaw so that the boxes balance? Explain your response.

   _____

6. A board is L feet long. Boxes A and B weigh 60 pounds and 80 pounds, respectively. Box A is placed x feet from the pivot point.

   a. Write and solve an equation for L in terms of x.   _____

   b. Write and solve an equation for x in terms of L.   _____

Algebra 1

Enrichment

11.2 *Exploring Functions Defined by Reciprocals*

The function $f(x) = x$ is a polynomial function. The function $g(x) = \frac{1}{x}$ is a rational function. The diagram at right shows the graphs of $f(x) = x$ and $g(x) = \frac{1}{x}$.

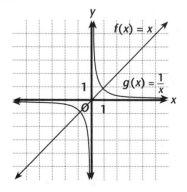

Notice that the graph of f is a continuous and straight line. The graph of g is neither continuous nor straight. Taking the reciprocal of x has the effect of breaking a straight line into two curved branches, each extending indefinitely. Notice also that the break occurs at $x = 0$, the only real number that has no reciprocal.

In Exercises 1 and 2, graph f and g on the same coordinate grid. For what value of x does the break occur?

1. $f(x) = x + 1$ and $g(x) = \frac{1}{x + 1}$

2. $f(x) = x - 1$ and $g(x) = \frac{1}{x - 1}$

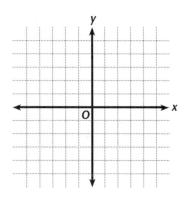

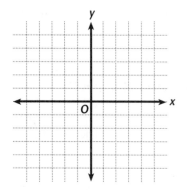

_____

_____

Graph each function and its reciprocal on the same coordinate grid.

3. $y = x - 2.5$

4. $y = x - 3$

5. $y = x + 3$

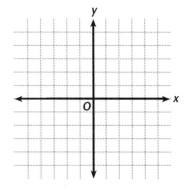

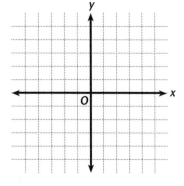

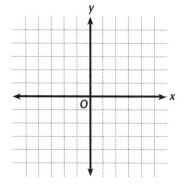

_____

_____

_____

Enrichment

11.3 Using Ratios to Compare Volumes and Surface Areas

Using ratios and formulas from geometry, you can compare measurements of geometric figures. The diagram at right shows a sphere fitting snugly inside of a cube. Each face of the cube touches the sphere in exactly one point. Some useful formulas from geometry are shown below.

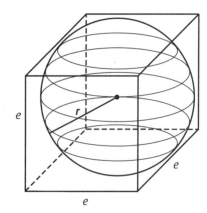

Cube: volume: $V_c = e^3$ surface area: $S_c = 6e^2$

Sphere: volume: $V_s = \frac{4}{3}\pi r^3$ surface area: $S_s = 4\pi r^2$

In the exercises that follow, *r* represents the radius of the sphere, and *e* represents the length of one edge of the cube.

1. Refer to the cross section shown at right. It results from a plane slicing straight down through the center of the sphere.

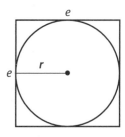

    a. Write an equation for *e* in terms of *r*. _____

    b. Write an equation for *r* in terms of *e*. _____

Write and simplify the specified ratio, *R*.

2. *R*: the volume of the sphere to the surface area of the sphere, using the variable *r* for the radius.

    _____

3. *R*: the volume of the cube to the surface area of the cube, using the variable *e* for the edge length.

    _____

Describe the rational function defined by each ratio. Sketch the graph of the function.

4. the ratio in Exercise 2

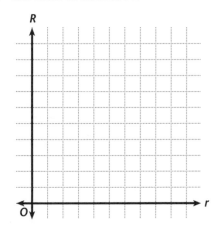

5. the ratio in Exercise 3

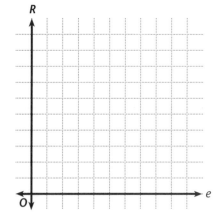

6. Compare the volume of a cube to that of a sphere. _____

Enrichment

11.4 *Finding Average Speed for an Extended Trip*

Jack Schmidt drove from his shop to a job site at an average speed of 55 miles per hour. He returned to his shop from that site by driving on the same highway at an average speed of 45 miles per hour. What was his average speed over the entire trip? To find out, you will need to write and simplify a rational expression for his average speed over the entire trip.

Refer to the problem above. Let *d* represent the length of the trip one way, t_1 represent his travel time to the job site, and t_2 represent his travel time back to the shop.

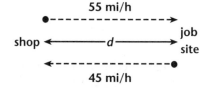

1. Explain how you know that $t_1 = \frac{d}{55}$ and $t_2 = \frac{d}{45}$.

_____

2. Use the expression $\frac{\text{total distance}}{\text{total time}}$ to find Jack Schmidt's average speed for the entire trip. Show your work in the space below.

$\left(\text{Hint:} \ \frac{\text{total distance}}{\text{total time}} = \frac{d + d}{t_1 + t_2} = \frac{d + d}{\frac{d}{55} + \frac{d}{45}} \right)$

_____

3. **a.** Suppose that Jack travels to the site at *r* miles per hour and returns at *s* miles per hour. Find his average speed for the entire trip by simplifying $\frac{d + d}{\frac{d}{r} + \frac{d}{s}}$.   _____

   b. How does your answer to part **a** show that Jack Schmidt's average speed for the entire trip is not the average of 45 miles per hour and 55 miles per hour?

_____

The diagram below shows an extended trip that Jack Schmidt recently made.

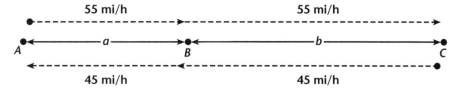

In Exercises 4 and 5, refer to the diagram above.

4. The expression at right represents his average speed for the trip from *A* to *B* to *C* and then back to *A*. Simplify the expression.

$\frac{a + b + b + a}{\frac{a}{55} + \frac{b}{55} + \frac{b}{45} + \frac{a}{45}}$

_____

5. Explain why the answer to Exercise 4 is the same as the answer to Exercise 2.

_____

Enrichment

11.5 Exploring Reciprocals, Rational Equations, and Integer Solutions

In Lesson 10.5, you learned how to solve rational equations in one variable. Each equation below is a rational equation in two variables, x and y.

$$\frac{1}{x} + \frac{1}{y} = 1 \qquad \frac{1}{x} + \frac{1}{y} = 2 \qquad \frac{1}{x} + \frac{1}{y} = \frac{1}{2}$$

In the exercises on this page, assume that x and y are positive integers.

Find one solution to each equation of the form $\frac{1}{x} + \frac{1}{y} = \frac{1}{n}$, where n is a positive integer.

1. $\frac{1}{x} + \frac{1}{y} = 1$ **2.** $\frac{1}{x} + \frac{1}{y} = \frac{1}{2}$ **3.** $\frac{1}{x} + \frac{1}{y} = \frac{1}{4}$

_____   _____   _____

4. $\frac{1}{x} + \frac{1}{y} = \frac{1}{6}$ **5.** $\frac{1}{x} + \frac{1}{y} = \frac{1}{8}$ **6.** $\frac{1}{x} + \frac{1}{y} = \frac{1}{100}$

_____   _____   _____

7. Suppose that you are given $\frac{1}{x} + \frac{1}{y} = \frac{1}{n}$, where n is an even positive integer. Based on your work in Exercises 1–6, write formulas in terms of n for x and for y.

_____

8. a. Let $\frac{1}{x} + \frac{1}{y} = 2$. Show that $x = 1$ and $y = 1$ are solutions to the equation by using substitution.

_____

b. If x and y are positive integers other than 1, then $0 < \frac{1}{x} < 1$ and $0 < \frac{1}{y} < 1$. Explain how this fact helps you show that there are no positive integer solutions to $\frac{1}{x} + \frac{1}{y} = 2$ other than $x = 1$ and $y = 1$.

_____

c. How does the reasoning in Part **b** help you show that, when n is an integer greater than 2 and x and y are positive integers, the equation $\frac{1}{x} + \frac{1}{y} = n$ has no integer solutions?

_____

Use trial and error to help you decide whether the given equation has any integer solutions. If so state one solution.

9. $\frac{1}{x} + \frac{1}{y} = \frac{1}{3}$ _____   **10.** $\frac{1}{x} + \frac{1}{y} = \frac{1}{5}$ _____

Enrichment

11.6 Exploring Flaws in Proofs

In mathematics, you often use logical reasoning. When you properly apply mathematical facts, your reasoning is sound. When you misapply mathematical facts, you can produce reasoning that is flawed.

Find the error(s) in reasoning in each logical argument.

1. If x is any real number, then $x \geq x$.

$$x \geq x$$
$$x \geq x - 1$$
$$x^2 \geq x^2 - x$$
$$0 \geq -x$$
$$0 \leq x$$

Therefore, all real numbers are nonnegative.

_____

2. If $a = b = 1$, then $a^2 = b^2 = 1$.
Thus, $a^2 - b^2 = 0$.
$$(a + b)(a - b) = 0$$
$$\frac{(a + b)(a - b)}{a - b} = \frac{0}{a - b}$$
$$\frac{(a + b)(\cancel{a - b})}{\cancel{a - b}} = \frac{0}{\cancel{a - b}}$$
$$a + b = 0$$
Because $a = b = 1$, $a + b = 2$.
Therefore, $2 = 0$.

_____

3. If r is a positive number, then $\sqrt{r} = r$.
$$\sqrt{r} = r$$
$$\frac{\sqrt{r}}{r} = 1$$
$$\left(\frac{\sqrt{r}}{r}\right)^2 = 1^2$$
$$\frac{r}{r^2} = 1$$
$$\frac{1}{r} = 1$$
$$r = 1$$
Therefore, all positive numbers equal 1.

_____

4. The graphs of the equations $\begin{cases} x + y = 2 \\ x + y = 6 \end{cases}$ in the system at right are parallel lines because the equations have the same slope. When you solve the system by substitution, you get $x + (x + 2) = 6$. Thus, $x = 2$. Solving for y, you get $2 + y = 2$. Thus, $y = 0$. Therefore, $(2, 0)$ lies on both lines. Therefore, there are two lines that are parallel and intersect at $(2, 0)$.

_____

5. Let $a = 1$ and $b = -1$.

$$a^2 = 1 \text{ and } b^2 = 1$$
$$a^2 = b^2$$
$$\sqrt{a^2} = \sqrt{b^2}$$
$$a = b$$
$$1 = -1$$

Therefore, 1 and -1 are the same.

_____

6. In $\triangle ABC$, angle C is a right angle, and each leg is a units long. By the Pythagorean theorem, $AB^2 = a^2 + a^2 = 2a^2$. Thus, $AB = \sqrt{2a^2} = 2a$. Therefore, in a right triangle whose legs have the same length, the hypotenuse is twice as long as a leg.

_____

7. Show logically that this question is nonsense.

| Last year, Mia was one year younger than Jon. Next year, they will be the same age. How old are they? |

_____

Enrichment

12.1 Exploring Conjugates of Radical Expressions

The radical expressions $3 + 5\sqrt{2}$ and $3 - 5\sqrt{2}$ are the same except for the subtraction. These numbers are *conjugates* of one another. When you add, subtract, multiply, or divide two numbers that are conjugates, you get special results.

Consider $3 + 5\sqrt{2}$ and $3 - 5\sqrt{2}$. Perform the specified operation.

1. $\left(3 + 5\sqrt{2}\right) + \left(3 - 5\sqrt{2}\right)$

_____

2. $\left(3 + 5\sqrt{2}\right) - \left(3 - 5\sqrt{2}\right)$

_____

3. $\left(3 + 5\sqrt{2}\right) \times \left(3 - 5\sqrt{2}\right)$

_____

4. $\left(3 + 5\sqrt{2}\right) \div \left(3 - 5\sqrt{2}\right)$

_____

Suppose that a and b are real numbers. Simplify each expression.

5. $\left(a + b\sqrt{2}\right) + \left(a - b\sqrt{2}\right)$

_____

6. $\left(a + b\sqrt{2}\right) - \left(a - b\sqrt{2}\right)$

_____

7. $\left(a + b\sqrt{2}\right) \times \left(a - b\sqrt{2}\right)$

_____

8. $\left(a + b\sqrt{2}\right) \div \left(a - b\sqrt{2}\right)$

_____

Suppose that a and b are real numbers and that n is not a perfect square.

9. What can you say about $\left(a + b\sqrt{n}\right)\left(a - b\sqrt{n}\right)$?

_____

10. Without multiplying, simplify $\left(2 + \sqrt{91}\right)\left(2 - \sqrt{91}\right)$.

_____

11. What can you say about $\dfrac{a + b\sqrt{n}}{a - b\sqrt{n}}$?

_____

12. Without dividing, simplify $\dfrac{2 + \sqrt{7}}{2 - \sqrt{7}}$.

_____

Enrichment

12.2 Exploring Radical Equations Arising from $y = \sqrt{x}$

The function $y = \sqrt{x}$ is the parent function from which you can write each of the functions below.

$$y = \sqrt{x} + 2 \qquad y = \sqrt{x} + 4 \qquad y = \sqrt{x} + 6$$
$$y = \sqrt{x - 2} \qquad y = \sqrt{x - 4} \qquad y = \sqrt{x - 6}$$

All six functions are graphed at right along with the parent function, which is darker than the other graphs.

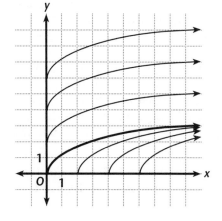

The graphs of $y = \sqrt{x} + 2$, $y = \sqrt{x} + 4$, and $y = \sqrt{x} + 6$ are the three curves directly above the graph of $y = \sqrt{x}$. Use the graphs to explain why the equations below have no solution.

1. $\sqrt{x} + 2 = \sqrt{x} + 4$

2. $\sqrt{x} + 2 = \sqrt{x} + 6$

3. $\sqrt{x} + 4 = \sqrt{x} + 6$

_____   _____   _____

_____   _____   _____

The graphs of $y = \sqrt{x - 2}$, $y = \sqrt{x - 4}$, and $y = \sqrt{x - 6}$ are the three curves below the graph of $y = \sqrt{x}$. Show algebraically that each equation below has no solution.

4. $\sqrt{x - 2} = \sqrt{x - 4}$

5. $\sqrt{x - 2} = \sqrt{x - 6}$

6. $\sqrt{x - 4} = \sqrt{x - 6}$

_____   _____   _____

_____   _____   _____

_____   _____   _____

The diagram above suggests that the graphs of $y = \sqrt{x - 2}$, $y = \sqrt{x - 4}$, and $y = \sqrt{x - 6}$ get closer to the graph of $y = \sqrt{x}$ as x gets larger.

7. Complete the table below. Round values to the nearest thousandth.

x	10	20	50	100	200	500	1000	5000
$\sqrt{x}$								
$\sqrt{x - 2}$								
$\sqrt{x} - \sqrt{x - 2}$								

8. Let n be a positive integer. Write and justify a conjecture about $\sqrt{x} - \sqrt{x - n}$.

_____

Enrichment

12.3 Exploring Different Proofs of the Pythagorean Theorem

In Lesson 12.3, you explored one proof of the Pythagorean Theorem. There
are many other proofs of the theorem. You can explore two of them in the
following exercises. For reference, the Pythagorean Theorem is illustrated
at right and stated below.

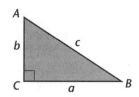

In $\triangle ABC$, which has a right angle at C, $a^2 + b^2 = c^2$.

Three area formulas that you will need are shown below.

> Square: Area = length of side squared   Triangle: Area = one-half base times height
> Trapezoid: Area = one-half the height times the sum of the bases

**In Exercises 1–3, two copies of $\triangle ABC$ have been positioned so
that the resulting figure is a trapezoid.**

1. **a.** The two horizontal line segments are the bases
    of the trapezoid. The vertical line segment is
    the height. Write an expression in terms
    of a and b for the area of the trapezoid shown. _____

    b. Simplify the expression that you wrote in part **a.** _____

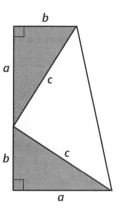

2. The trapezoid consists of two copies of the right triangle shown above
    and a right triangle whose legs are c units long. Write and simplify an
    expression for the sum of the areas of the three triangles.

    _____

3. Explain how your work in Exercises 1 and 2 prove the Pythagorean Theorem.

    _____

**In Exercises 4–6, four copies of $\triangle ABC$ have been positioned so
that the resulting figure is a square.**

4. Write an expression for the area of the
    entire square including the white square. _____

5. **a.** Find the dimensions of the
    white square. _____

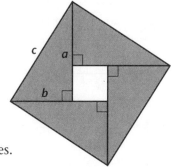

    b. Write and simplify an expression for
    the area of the white square. _____

6. Write and simplify an expression for the total area of the four triangles.

    _____

7. Explain how your work in Exercises 4, 5, and 6 prove the Pythagorean Theorem.

    _____

Enrichment

12.4 Exploring a Non-Pythagorean Distance Formula

The distance formula that you learned in Lesson 12.4 is an example of a function that assigns a nonnegative number to be the measure of distance, d, between the two given points in a plane. The function below is another distance function that you can use to find the distance, d', between $P_1(x_1, y_1)$ and $P_2(x_2, y_2)$.

$$d' = |x_2 - x_1| + |y_2 - y_1|$$

To find d', find the sum of the lengths of the legs in a right triangle.

The streets of Manhattan, New York, are laid out in a rectangular grid. Taxis travel from one point to another by traveling along the legs of a right triangle. Therefore, some people call this distance function the *Manhattan distance function*.

In Exercises 1–4, use the Manhattan distance function to find the distance that a taxicab needs to travel to get from P_1 to P_2.

1. $P_1(0, 0)$ and $P_2(4, 3)$ _____

2. $P_1(-3, -5)$ and $P_2(4, 3)$ _____

3. $P_1(-4, 3)$ and $P_2(4; 3)$ _____

4. $P_1(4, -5)$ and $P_2(4, 3)$ _____

5. Maggie argued that the distance between two points found by using the Manhattan distance function is always greater than that found by using the Pythagorean Theorem. Michael argued that the distances are sometimes the same. Who do you agree with? Explain your response.

_____

6. The Pythagorean distance formula gives you a nonnegative number. Explain why the Manhattan distance function also gives you a nonnegative measure of the distance between two points.

_____

Find the distance between R and S by finding the length of the path from R to S. Then verify that the Manhattan distance function gives the same distance.

7.

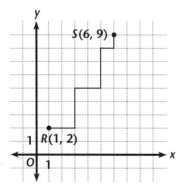

8.

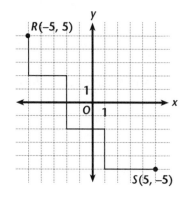

_____   _____

Enrichment

12.5 *Exploring Midpoints of Sides in Triangles*

Now that you know how to find the coordinates of the midpoint
of a line segment, you can use midpoints to explore geometric
properties of triangles. For reference, the midpoint formula
is stated below.

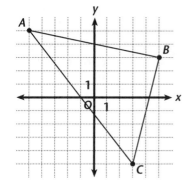

The coordinates of the midpoint, *M,* of $\overline{PQ}$ are $M = \left(\dfrac{x_1 + x_2}{2}, \dfrac{y_1 + y_2}{2} \right)$.

Refer to the diagram at right.

1. Find the coordinates of the midpoints M_1, M_2, and M_3 of the
    three sides $\overline{AC}$, $\overline{AB}$, and $\overline{BC}$, respectively. List the coordinates
    and graph them on the diagram at right.

    _____

2. **a.** On the diagram at right above, carefully draw $\overline{M_1B}$, $\overline{M_2C}$, and $\overline{M_3A}$.
    b. Do the line segments appear to meet in a point? Explain your
    response.

    _____

You can use systems of equations to explore how the lines containing $\overline{M_1B}$,
$\overline{M_2C}$, and $\overline{M_3A}$ are related.

Write an equation for the line containing each line segment.

3. $\overline{M_1B}$ 4. $\overline{M_2C}$ 5. $\overline{M_3A}$

    _____   _____   _____

**Write and solve a system of equations for the lines containing
each pair of segments.**

6. $\overline{M_1B}$ and $\overline{M_2C}$ _____   7. $\overline{M_2C}$ and $\overline{M_3A}$ _____

8. How do your solutions in Exercises 6 and 7 confirm your observation
    from part **b** of Exercise 2.

    _____

9. Connect M_1, M_2, and M_3 in order to form $\triangle M_1M_2M_3$. How is $\triangle M_1M_2M_3$
    related to $\triangle ABC$?

    _____

    _____

Enrichment

12.6 Exploring Slopes and Tangents

When you graph an equation that represents a line that is not vertical, you get a line that is slanted up to the right, is horizontal, or is slanted down to the right. These three situations are shown in the graph at left below. The graph shows that $y = 2x + 3$ slants up to the right, that $y = 3$ is horizontal, and that $y = -x + 3$ slants down to the right.

Using the tangent, you can make a connection between the slope of a line and the angle that the line makes with the horizontal. To make the connection, draw a right triangle whose hypotenuse lies along the graph of the equation. A triangle for the graph of $y = 2x + 3$ is shown at right below.

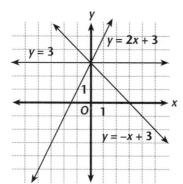 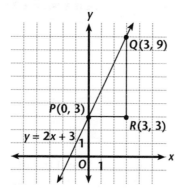

a. **Graph each equation on the grid provided.**   **b.** **Find the slope of the line.**
c. **Find the tangent of $\angle QPR$ by using a right triangle.**

1. $y = 3x - 2$ **2.** $y = 1.5x + 1$ **3.** $y = 0.25x + 2$

_____   _____   _____

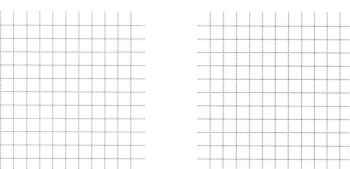

4. Based on your work in Exercises 1–3, write a conjecture that relates the slope of a linear equation to the tangent of the angle that the line makes with the horizontal.

_____

5. Explain how to find the measure of the angle that the graph of $y = 2.4x + 5.3$ makes with the horizontal. What is the measure of that angle to the nearest tenth of a degree?

_____

Enrichment

12.7 Using Trigonometric Ratios in Nested Right Triangles

The diagram at right shows a lighthouse at point
D atop a vertical cliff whose base, C, is at sea level.
Points A and B represent the locations of ships
whose captains sight the lighthouse at angles of
elevation of 20° and 42°, respectively.

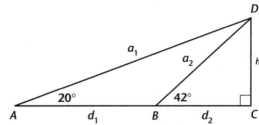

**Refer to the diagram at right. Assume
that the height of the cliff is 200 feet.
Use a trigonometric ratio to find each
length. Round answers to the nearest tenth of a foot.**

1. BC in $\triangle DBC$

_____

2. AC in $\triangle ADC$

_____

3. BD in $\triangle DBC$

_____

4. AD in $\triangle ADC$

_____

5. a. Using answers from Exercises 1–4, find the distance AB.
  Round your answer to the nearest tenth of a foot.   _____

  b. Using trigonometric ratios, write an equation
  that gives d_1, or AB, in terms of h, 20°, and 42°.   _____

**In Exercises 6–8, specific values of some variables in the diagram
are given. Solve each problem.**

6. A lighthouse keeper at point D sights a ship at point B. The sight line
forms a 20° angle with the calm sea. The lighthouse keeper is 125 feet above
sea level. How far from the base of the cliff, point C, is the ship when it
is at point B?   _____

7. A ship is at point A, 5000 feet from the base of the cliff at point C.
Find the distance between the ship at point A and the ship at point B.   _____

8. The captain of a ship at point A sights a lighthouse at point D. After
traveling 1600 yards closer to shore along a straight course, the captain
sights the lighthouse at a 42°-angle of elevation.

  a. Justify the two equations at right.

  | $h = (1600 + d_2) \tan 20°$ |
  | $h = d_2 \tan 42°$ |

_____

_____

  b. Explain how the two equations at right above give $h = 1600 \times \tan 20° + h\left(\dfrac{\tan 20°}{\tan 42°}\right)$.

_____

  c. Find the height of the cliff. _____

Enrichment

12.8 *Exploring Operations on Special Matrices*

Matrix R shown at the right is called a diagonal matrix with a and b along its *main diagonal*. A **diagonal matrix** is a square matrix whose elements off of the main diagonal are all 0.

$$R = \begin{bmatrix} a & 0 \\ 0 & b \end{bmatrix}$$

Let $R = \begin{bmatrix} a & 0 \\ 0 & b \end{bmatrix}$ and $S = \begin{bmatrix} c & 0 \\ 0 & d \end{bmatrix}$

1. a. Find $R + S$. _____

  b. Is $R + S$ a diagonal matrix? Explain your response. _____

2. a. Find RS. _____

  b. Is RS a diagonal matrix? Explain your response. _____

3. A set of objects is **closed** under addition, or multiplication, if the result of the operation is always another member of the set. Is the set of 2×2 diagonal matrices closed under addition? under multiplication? Explain your response.

_____

4. Let $R = \begin{bmatrix} a & 0 \\ 0 & b \end{bmatrix}$, where $a \neq 0$ and $b \neq 0$. Let $T = \begin{bmatrix} \frac{1}{a} & 0 \\ 0 & \frac{1}{b} \end{bmatrix}$ and let $I = \begin{bmatrix} 1 & 0 \\ 0 & 1 \end{bmatrix}$.

  a. Find RT and TR. _____
  b. What do these products tell you about R and T?

_____

5. Suppose that $\begin{bmatrix} a & 0 \\ 0 & b \end{bmatrix} \begin{bmatrix} a & 0 \\ 0 & b \end{bmatrix} = \begin{bmatrix} 1 & 0 \\ 0 & 1 \end{bmatrix}$. What must be true of a and b? _____

Just as you can explore sums and products of 2×2 diagonal matrices, you can explore 3×3 diagonal matrices. Shown at the right is a 3×3 diagonal matrix M.

$$M = \begin{bmatrix} a & 0 & 0 \\ 0 & b & 0 \\ 0 & 0 & c \end{bmatrix}$$

6. Write conjectures about sums and products of two 3×3 diagonal matrices.

  sums: _____

  products: _____

7. Find N such that $MN = \begin{bmatrix} 1 & 0 & 0 \\ 0 & 1 & 0 \\ 0 & 0 & 1 \end{bmatrix}$. _____

Enrichment

13.1 Exploring a Game-Show Probability Function

The wheel shown at right is similar to those used on game shows.

Consider a game-show function that has as its domain the dollar amounts that you could win with one spin of the wheel.

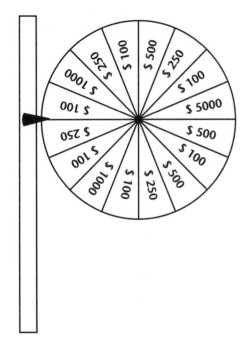

1. Write the domain of the function.

_____

This game-show function will assign a number to the probability of landing on each dollar amount. For example, since 6 out of 16 spins are labeled with $100, the theoretical probability of landing on a space marked with $100 is $\frac{6}{16}$ or $\frac{3}{8}$.   Thus, $P(100) = \frac{3}{8}$.

Complete each of the following.

2. $P(250) = $ _____   **3.** $P(500) = $ _____   **4.** $P(1000) = $ _____   **5.** $P(5000) = $ _____

6. What is the range of this function? _____

This function has a special property.

7. What is the sum of all the range elements for this function? _____

8. Why does the sum have to be the number that you found in Exercise 7?

_____

9. Is the sum of the range elements for any function always this number? Explain your response.

_____

For this game-show function find each of the following probabilities.

10. $P(100 \text{ or } 500)$ _____   **11.** $P(500 \text{ or } 1000)$ _____

12. $P(\text{more than } 500)$ _____   **13.** $P(\text{at least } 500)$ _____

14. $P(\text{less than } 500)$ _____   **15.** $P(10{,}000)$ _____

Enrichment
13.2 Venn Diagrams and Probability

Three classes, French, biology, and geography, got together after school to have an academic contest. They used practice questions for a national scholastic test. These classes normally meet at different times of the day, so some students are in more than one of these classes.

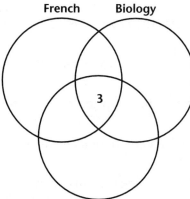

Here are the facts.

- There are 22 students in the French class.
- There are 25 students in the biology class.
- There are 24 students in the geography class.

- 8 of these students are in both the French class and the biology class.
- 11 of these students are in both the biology class and the geography class.
- 5 of these students are in both the French class and the geography class.

- 3 students are in all 3 classes

The 3 students that are in all three classes are represented in the Venn diagram at the intersection of all 3 of the circles.

1. Use the above facts to place numbers that represent students in each of the remaining 6 sections of the Venn diagram.

2. What is the total number of students represented in the diagram? _____

Assume that all students are equally likely to win the first-place medal. What is the probability that the first-place student was

3. in the French class?   _____

4. in the biology class?   _____

5. in biology but neither of the other classes?   _____

6. in French but neither of the other classes?   _____

7. not in French?   _____

8. not in biology?   _____

9. in only 1 of these classes?   _____

10. in exactly 2 of these classes?   _____

Enrichment

13.3 Counting Paths in a Tree Diagram

Suppose that you have just won a contest and may pick a new car as your prize. The prize car is a convertible and has the following color choices:

body color: white, red, green, or black

convertible top color: white, red, or black

interior color: red, green, or black

1. Assume that all combinations of body, convertible top, and interior colors are available. Use abbreviations, such as R for red, to complete a tree diagram.

2. How many different combinations are possible? _____

Although we assumed that all combinations were possible, some of these combinations might not be pleasing to you.

How many car choices would there be if

3. the body, top, and interior must all be the same color?   _____

4. the body, top, and interior must not all be the same color? _____

5. you do not want a car with white on any of the 3 parts?   _____

6. the interior must be red or green?   _____

7. you want all 3 colors to be different?   _____

Enrichment

13.4 Drawing Without Replacement

It is dark when you stumble out of bed and you are not ready to turn on the light. You pick socks out of the sock drawer at random. The wash has just been done, so you know that there are 8 blue, 4 tan, and 12 white socks in the drawer.

1. What is the probability that the first sock that you pick is blue?   _____

2. If the first sock that you picked was blue, and you hold onto it, what is the probability that the second sock that you pick will also be blue?   _____

3. What is the probability that you picked 2 blue socks?   _____

4. Using the same process that you used for Exercises 1–3 and starting over with a full drawer of socks, what is the probability of picking 2 socks, without replacement, that both are white?   _____

Suppose that there are *n* socks in another drawer and that 6 of them are brown. (Assume that there are more than 6 socks in the drawer.)

5. What is the probability of picking 1 brown sock?   _____

6. If the first sock that you picked was brown, and you hold onto it, what is the probability that the second sock that you picked will also be brown?   _____

7. What is the probability of picking 2 brown socks if the first one is not replaced?   _____

There are tryouts for seating positions in band. To determine the order of the *n* students trying out, slips of paper numbered 1 through *n* are placed in the bag, and each student draws a number.

8. What is the probability that the first number drawn is 8? (Assume that there are at least 8 students.)   _____

9. If the first student draws position 8, what is the probability that the next student will draw 5?   _____

10. If the slips with 8 and 5 have been drawn, what is the probability that the number 4 will be drawn next?   _____

11. Find the probability that the slips with 8, 5, and 4 are selected in this order?   _____

12. Suppose you want to draw the number 1 so that you can play first. As other students draw other numbers, what happens to your chances of getting the 1?

_____

Enrichment
13.5 *A Driving Simulation*

A group of students has decided to make a video simulation for a drivers' training class. They plan to have the video shown as students sit at a simulation desk that has a steering wheel, brake pedal, accelerator, and turn signals. The group decides that the simulation video will give a view of the windshield, the rear and side view mirrors, and instruments on the dashboard.

Your task is to determine what types of activities should be included in the video simulation of traffic situations.

To make your task more manageable, you have decided to first consider what you believe to be the qualities of a good driver. These might include items such as knowledge of traffic signs and laws, ability to concentrate on driving, showing courtesy to others, and so on.

1. Make a list of six qualities that you feel are important for a good driver to possess.

    a. _____

    b. _____

    c. _____

    d. _____

    e. _____

    f. _____

For each quality, you will need to devise some type of activity that will test the driver. For example, a triangular-shaped YIELD sign could appear on the right. An appropriate response would be to slow down and look for traffic coming from the right.

2. For each quality you listed in Exercise 1, suggest a test activity and a sample appropriate response.

    a. **test activity** _____ **response** _____

    b. **test activity** _____ **response** _____

    c. **test activity** _____ **response** _____

    d. **test activity** _____ **response** _____

    e. **test activity** _____ **response** _____

    f. **test activity** _____ **response** _____

Enrichment
14.1 *Functioning in the Real World*

A Celsius thermometer shows a reading of 40°C. While you are looking at this thermometer, the local weather report on the radio gives a temperature of 104°F. When you change to another local station, you hear a report of 112°F.

1. Use the formula $F = \frac{9}{5}C + 32$ to find the Fahrenheit temperature

   corresponding to 40°C. _____

2. Why do you suppose that you heard a different Fahrenheit temperature on one of the radio stations?

   _____

3. Explain why $F = \frac{9}{5}C + 32$ represents a function.

   _____

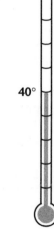

40°

4. Complete the following ordered pairs for (C, F) by using the formula
   $F = \frac{9}{5}C + 32$:

   a. (25,   )   **b.** (−10,   )   **c.** (18,   )   **d.** (, 86)

5. In part **d** of Exercise 4, you solved for C given F. Use the appropriate
   properties of equality to solve $F = \frac{9}{5}C + 32$ for C in terms of F. _____

6. Use the formula found in Exercise 5 to complete the following ordered pairs.

   a. (, 59)   **b.** (, 77)   **c.** (, −4)   **d.** (, 80)

7. Is this formula for C in terms of F also a function? Why or why not?

   _____

8. Functions that "undo" each other are called *inverse* functions. Start
   with 35°C and use the first formula to find a value of F. Then use this
   value of F in the second formula to find a value of C. What happens?

   _____

9. Find the temperature at which the Celsius and the Fahrenheit
   temperatures are equivalent.

   _____

Enrichment

14.2 *Periodic Functions*

1. How does the graph of $y = (x - 2)^2$ compare to the graph of $y = x^2$?

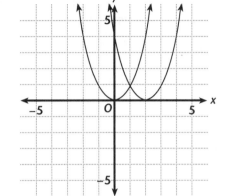

_____

2. Describe the graph of a general function $y = (x - n)^2$, where n could be any integer.

_____

Recall that a statement such as $-2 \leq x < 2$ means that x is restricted to real number values between -2 and 2, where -2 is included, but 2 is not.

3. Describe what the graph of $y = x^2$ looks like if the domain is restricted by $-2 \leq x < 2$.

_____

4. Complete the following table for the function $y = (x - 2)^2$, where $1 \leq x < 5$:

x	1	1.5	2	2.5	3	3.5	4	4.5
y								

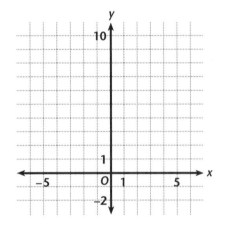

5. Use the grid at right to graph the points in the table, and connect them with a smooth curve.

6. As a challenge, graph the following three functions on the same grid at right:

$y = (x - n)^2$, where $n - 2 \leq x < n + 2$
   and $n = 0, 4, 8$

This means that you should let $n = 0$ and draw a graph; then let $n = 4$ and draw another graph on the same grid, and then do likewise for $n = 8$. Your graph should have 3 "pieces."

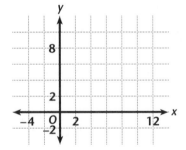

If you allowed n to take on all the multiples of 4 as values, you could construct what is called a *periodic* function.

To see another example of a periodic function, use your graphics calculator to draw a graph of $y = \sin x$. (*sin* stands for the trigonometric function sine.)

7. In your own words, describe what you think a periodic function is.

_____

Enrichment

14.3 Stretching and Compressing

The table at right contains the coordinates of the vertices of rectangle *ABCD* shown in the two graphs below.

x	−1	4	4	−1
y	−1	−1	2	2

1. Complete the following table by multiplying each of the *x*-coordinates in the table by 2 and each of the *y*-coordinates in the table by 0.5.

$$(x, y) \rightarrow (2x, 0.5y)$$

x				
y				

2. Complete the following table by replacing the *x*- and *y*-coordinates as indicated by

$$(x, y) \rightarrow (x + y, y)$$

x				
y				

3. On the same grid, sketch a graph of another rectangle using the coordinates you found in Exercise 1.

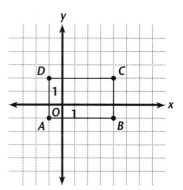

4. On the same grid, sketch a graph of another rectangle by using the coordinates that you found in Exercise 2.

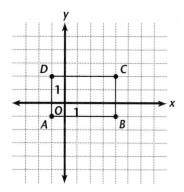

5. Describe how the new rectangle in Exercise 3 relates to rectangle *ABCD*.

_____

6. Describe the shape of the figure that you drew in Exercise 4 and how it relates to rectangle *ABCD*.

_____

There are several ways to change rectangle *EFGH* into a square by stretching or compressing.

7. Experiment and then describe two different ways to transform rectangle *EFGH* into a square.

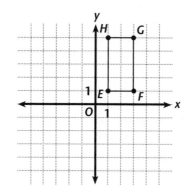

a. _____

b. _____

Enrichment

14.4 *Symmetrical Figures*

The solid-line figure that contains points *A, B, C,* and *D* has been reflected across line ℓ, creating the figure that contains points *A', B', C',* and *D'.* Notice that ℓ is the line of symmetry.

Recall that the *distance* from a point to a line is the perpendicular distance between them.

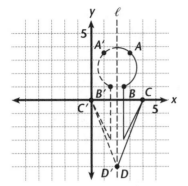

1. How does the distance from *A'* to ℓ compare with the distance from ℓ to *A*? _____

2. What is the geometric relationship between $\overline{A'A}$ and line ℓ? _____

3. What do Exercises 1 and 2 tell you about locating point *B'* given point *B*?

Using the tools available to you, carefully reflect each figure below across the specified line.

4.

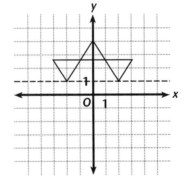

5.

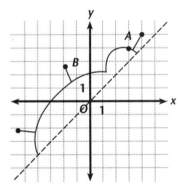

Reflections across the line *y = x,* as in Exercise 5, are called *inverses* of each other.

6. In Exercise 5 mark points *A'* and *B'.* Compare the coordinates of points *A* and *A'* and also *B* and *B'.* Using these points and any other pairs of symmetrical points that you observe, make a conjecture about ordered pairs for reflected points in inverse relations.

_____

_____

Enrichment

14.5 Transformation Designs

1. This graph shows the function $y = |x| + 1$.

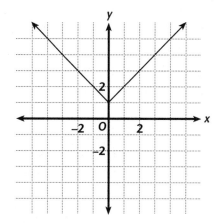

It may help to use tracing paper to complete the following steps:

1. Draw the line $y = -x$.
2. Draw the reflection of the given function across this line. (The result should be a V opening to the left.)
3. Draw the line $y = x$.
4. Reflect the result of Step 2 across this line.
5. Reflect the result of Step 4 across the line $y = -x$.

Brighten your design with some colored pencils.

Follow the same steps as above for each function below. In some cases, you may wish to draw the lines $y = x$ and $y = -x$ lightly so that you can erase them from the final design.

2. $y = 0.5|x| + 1$

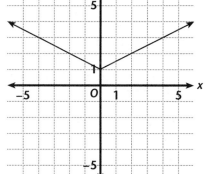

3. $y = \frac{1}{8}x^2$

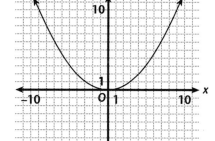

4. $y = x^2 - 2$

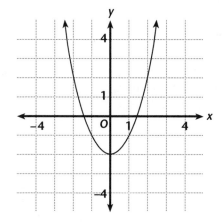

5. Try a function of your own.

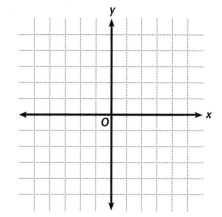

ANSWERS

Enrichment — Chapter 1

Lesson 1.1

1. $0, 0, 0, 0, \ldots$ 2. $1, 0, 1, 0, \ldots$

3. $1, 2, 0, 1, 2, \ldots$

4. $1, 2, 3, 0, 1, 2, 3, \ldots$

5. $1, 2, 3, 4, 0, 1, 2, 3, 4, \ldots$

6. $1, 2, 3, 4, 5, 0, 1, 2, 3, 4, 5, \ldots$

7. **a.** The sequence will range from 0 to 11
   and then repeat the pattern from 0 to 11.
   $1, 2, 3, 4, 5, 6, 7, 8, 9, 10, 11, 0, 1, 2, 3, 4,$
   $5, 6, 7, 8, 9, 10, 11, \ldots$
   b. The remainder will always be a whole
   number ranging from 0 to 1 less than
   the divisor. The remainders repeat
   because every whole number is some
   multiple of the divisor plus some whole
   number between 1 and 1 less than the
   divisor inclusive.

8. **a.** 10
   b. Every whole number divided by 10 will
   give a remainder that is a whole number
   from 0 to 9 inclusive.

9. 3:00 P.M.

Lesson 1.2

1. $5 + 5 + 5 + 5$ 2. $6 + 6 + 6 + 6 + 6$

3. $7 + 7 + 7 + 7 + 7 + 7$ 4. 4×5

5. 5×6 6. 6×7 7. $4 \times 5 \div 2 = 10$

8. $5 \times 6 \div 2 = 15$ 9. $6 \times 7 \div 2 = 21$

10. **a.** $(n + 1) + (n + 1) + \ldots + (n + 1)$
    with $n + 1$ occurring n times
    b. $\frac{n(n + 1)}{2}$ **c.** $\frac{100(100 + 1)}{2} = 5050$

11. $2 \times \frac{n(n + 1)}{2} = n(n + 1)$

Lesson 1.3

1. 6   2. $(10 + 20) \div 5 \times 2 = 12$ 3. $\times, -$

4. $\times, \div, \div$ 5. $\div, \times, \times$ 6. $\times, -, \div$

7. $-, \times, -$ 8. $1 = 3 - (3 \div 3) - (3 \div 3)$

9. $2 = 33 \div 3 - (3 \times 3)$

10. $3 = 3 + 3 + 3 - 3 - 3$

11. $4 = 3 \div 3 + 3 + 3 - 3$

12. $5 = 3 \div 3 + 3 \div 3 + 3$

13. $6 = 3 \times (3 - 3) + 3 + 3$

14. $7 = 3 \times 3 - 3 + (3 \div 3)$

15. $8 = (3 + 3) \div 3 + 3 + 3$

16. $9 = 3 + 3 + 3 + 3 - 3$

17. $10 = 3 \div 3 + 3 + 3 + 3$

Lesson 1.4

1. 3   2. $\frac{1}{3}$ 3. $(3, 1), (9, 1), (9, 3),$ and $(3, 3)$

4. The multiplication stretches the original
   square horizontally.

5. $(1, 3), (3, 3), (3, 9),$ and $(1, 9)$

6. The multiplication stretches the original
   square vertically.

7. $(1, 2), (4, 1),$ and $(2, 3)$

8. The division shrinks the original triangle
   horizontally and vertically by a factor of
   0.5.

9. Multiplication of coordinates by -1 results
   in a reflection of the original figure
   through the origin, the point $(0, 0)$.

Lesson 1.5

1. 64 cubic inches   2. 72 cubic inches

3. 48 cubic inches   4. 16 cubic inches

ANSWERS

5. 71.2 cubic inches **6.** 72.6 cubic inches

7. 73.5 cubic inches **8.** 74.0 cubic inches

9. 74.1 cubic inches **10.** 73.7 cubic inches

11. $x = 1.7$ inches

12. about 74.1 cubic inches

13. 1157.4 cubic inches

Lesson 1.6

1. a–b.

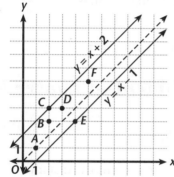

c. Yes, all the data points are either on the lines or between them.

2. a. 3 units **b.** 2 units

3.

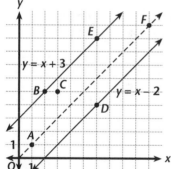

4. The closer together the parallel bounding lines are, the more tightly the data cluster around a line. The farther apart the parallel bounding lines are, the more loosely the data points cluster around a line.

Enrichment—Chapter 2

Lesson 2.1

1. rational **2.** irrational

3. rational **4.** irrational

5. Follow the three 0s with 12, then follow with four 0s, then 12, then five 0s, and so on.

6. Increase the number of 0s preceding 1 by 1 each time.

7. Follow with a 0, then five 5s, then 0, then six 5s, and so on.

8. Follow with four 5s, then four 0s, then five 5s, then 5 0s, and so on.

9. $0.\overline{5}$ **10.** $0.\overline{6}$

Lesson 2.2

1. $12 + 4.5$ **2.** $12 - 1.4$ **3.** $12 - 15$

4. $12 + 15$

5. Its speed would be 6 miles per hour.

6. Boat upstream: 2.5 miles per hour
Boat downstream: 11.5 miles per hour

7. Tim's speed is 1.8 miles per hour slower than Jack's.

8. Jack's speed is 1.8 miles per hour faster than Tim's.

9. Tim's parents are traveling 43.9 miles per hour faster than Tim.

Lesson 2.3

1. 4 **2.** 5 **3.** 9 **4.** 53 **5.** 134

6. 1334 **7.** 2 **8.** 1 **9.** 4 **10.** 15

11. 12 **12.** 2 **13.** $-110 < b < 10$

ANSWERS

Lesson 2.4

1. $-4, 12$ **2.** $6, 24$ **3.** $10, -30$

4. $-6, -30$ **5.** $12, 84$ **6.** $10, -100$

7. Rule: When multiplying three real numbers, multiply any two of them and then multiply the result by the third. In a product of several real numbers, a product with an even number of negative signs yields a positive answer, while a product with an odd number of negative signs yields a negative answer.

8. There are an odd number of negative signs, so the product is negative.

9. The product is negative because there is an odd number of negative signs.

10. If $n = 3, 7, 11, \ldots$, the product is negative. If $n = 1, 5, 9, 13, \ldots$, the product is positive.

Lesson 2.5

1. rx **2.** xs **3.** ry **4.** sy

5. a. sum: $rx + sx$
   product: $x(r + s)$
   b. $rx + sx = x(r + s)$
   c. Distributive Property

6. a. $x(r + s) + y(r + s)$
   b. First multiply x by the expression $r + s$ and then y by the expression $r + s$;
   $rx + sx + ry + sy$.
   c. $r(x + y) + s(x + y)$
   d. First multiply r by the expression $x + y$ and s by the expression $x + y$;
   $rx + sx + ry + sy$.

Lesson 2.6

1. $5x - 6$ **2.** $10x - 10$ **3.** $4x$

4. a. $44x - 32$ **b.** 130 units

5. $3.5x$ **6.** $10.5x - 2$ **7.** $51x$ **8.** 204

9. 2448 units

Lesson 2.7

1. a. $108x - 72$ **b.** $36 - 9x$
   c. $117x - 108$

2. because there is only one substitution in the answer to part **c**.

3. 15

4. $5x(4x - 3) - 15x^2 = 5x^2 - 15x$

5. rectangle: $2(5x) = 10x$
   and $2(4x - 3) = 8x - 6$
   shaded square: x by x

6. a. 70
   b. $10x(8x - 6) - 70x^2 = 10x^2 - 60x$

Enrichment—Chapter 3

Lesson 3.1

1. a. Let x represent the distance traveled.
   $37{,}538 + x = 37{,}781$
   b. 243 miles

2. $s + d = e$

3. a. $e - d$ **b.** $e - s$ **c.** $s + d$

4. a. $d = 1697$ **b.** $s = 17{,}242$
   c. $e = 63{,}777$ **d.** $d = 1111$

5. $7\frac{2}{3}$ feet

6. $f = o + d, o = f - d,$ and $d = f - o$

7. $9\frac{5}{12}$ feet

Lesson 3.2

1. $x = 3$ **2.** $x = -5$ **3.** $x = 3$ **4.** $t = \frac{6}{5}$

5. $w = \frac{1}{2}$ **6.** $d = 30$

ANSWERS

7. $$ax = b$$
$$\frac{1}{a} \cdot ax = \frac{1}{a} \cdot b$$
$$1 \cdot x = \frac{1}{a} \cdot b$$
$$x = \frac{b}{a}$$

8. $$\frac{ax}{a} = \frac{b}{a}$$
$$1x = \frac{b}{a}$$
$$x = \frac{b}{a}$$

9. Using the Multiplication Property of Equality, multiply each side of the equation by the reciprocal of the coefficient of the x-term.
Using the Division Property of Equality, divide each side of the equation by the coefficient of the x-term.
By either method, the solution is the same.

Lesson 3.3

1. 4 inches   2. 8 inches   3. 1 inch

4. 9 inches   5. 15 inches   6. 7 inches

7. 3 inches   8. 7 inches   9. 6 inches

10. 11 inches   11. 15 inches   12. 4 inches

13. 5 sides   14. 12 sides   15. 7 sides

16. 18 sides

Lesson 3.4

1. $x = -\frac{7}{3}$ 2. $x = -4$ 3. $x = 7\frac{1}{2}$

4. $x = -2$ 5. $2x + (-6) = 0$, or $-2x + 6 = 0$

6. $9x + 18 = 0$, or $-9x + (-18) = 0$

7. $5x + 27 = 0$, or $-5x + (-27) = 0$

8. $3x + (-21) = 0$, or $-3x + 21 = 0$

9. **a.** $x = -\frac{b}{a}$
   b. After writing the equation in the form $ax + b = 0$, substitute the values of a and b into the formula found in part **a.**

10. $x = 3$ 11. $x = -2$ 12. $x = -5\frac{2}{5}$

13. $x = 7$

14. **a.** infinitely many solutions
    b. no solutions

Lesson 3.5

1.

	Original amount	First location	Second location	Third location
Duty paid	0	$\frac{1}{3}x$	$\frac{1}{4} \cdot \frac{2}{3}x$	$\frac{1}{5} \cdot \frac{3}{4} \cdot \frac{2}{3}x$
Remaining goods	x	$\frac{2}{3}x$	$\frac{3}{4} \cdot \frac{2}{3}x$	$\frac{4}{5} \cdot \frac{3}{4} \cdot \frac{2}{3}x$

2. $x = 40$

3. Sample answer:
$$x - \frac{1}{6}x - \frac{1}{5} \cdot \frac{5}{6}x - \frac{1}{4} \cdot \frac{4}{5} \cdot \frac{5}{6}x - \frac{1}{3} \cdot \frac{3}{4} \cdot \frac{4}{5} \cdot$$
$$\frac{5}{6}x - \frac{1}{2} \cdot \frac{2}{3} \cdot \frac{3}{4} \cdot \frac{4}{5} \cdot \frac{5}{6}x = 3;$$
$$x = 18$$

4. Answers may vary. Sample answer: I prefer the modern method because the ancient method is too confusing.

Lesson 3.6

1. $I = 375$ 2. $P = 2000$ 3. $t = 5$ years

4. $r = 0.032$, or 3.2%   5. $351   6. 3 years

7. $2200   8. 0.03, or 3%   9. $247

10. 5 years   11. 0.027, or 2.7%

Enrichment—Chapter 4

Lesson 4.1

1. bc: $7 \times 15 = 105$
   ad: $5 \times 21 = 105$

2. **a.** Multiply each side by $\frac{bd}{ac}$.
   b. Cross-Product Property
   Multiplication Property of Equality
   Identity Property of Multiplication

ANSWERS

3.
$$\frac{a}{b} = \frac{c}{d}$$
$$ad = bc \quad \text{Cross-Product Property}$$
$$\left(\frac{1}{ab}\right)ad = \left(\frac{1}{ab}\right)bc \quad \begin{array}{l}\text{Multiplication}\\\text{Property of Equality}\end{array}$$
$$\frac{d}{b} = \frac{c}{a} \quad \begin{array}{l}\text{Identity Property of}\\\text{Multiplication}\end{array}$$

4.
$$\frac{a}{b} = \frac{c}{d}$$
$$\frac{a}{b} + 1 = \frac{c}{d} + 1 \quad \begin{array}{l}\text{Addition Property of}\\\text{Equality}\end{array}$$
$$\frac{a}{b} + \frac{b}{b} = \frac{c}{d} + \frac{d}{d} \quad \text{Rewrite 1.}$$
$$\frac{a + b}{b} = \frac{c + d}{d} \quad \text{addition}$$

5.
$$\frac{a}{b} = \frac{c}{d}$$
$$\frac{a}{b} - 1 = \frac{c}{d} - 1 \quad \begin{array}{l}\text{Subtraction Property of}\\\text{Equality}\end{array}$$
$$\frac{a}{b} - \frac{b}{b} = \frac{c}{d} - \frac{d}{d} \quad \text{Rewrite 1.}$$
$$\frac{a - b}{b} = \frac{c - d}{d} \quad \text{subtraction}$$

Lesson 4.2

1. $162.50   2. $97.50

3. 85% of $130 is $110.50, not $97.50

4. a 30% markup followed by a 15% markdown

5. Multiply the original amount by one plus the decimal or fractional form of the markup and then multiply that amount by one minus the decimal or fractional form of the markdown.

6. $97.50   7. $58.50

8. a 30% markdown followed by a 15% markdown

9. Multiply the original amount by one minus the decimal or fractional form of the markdown and then multiply that amount by one minus the decimal or fractional form of the markdown.

Lesson 4.3

1. A probability must be nonnegative because neither the number of favorable outcomes nor the number of total outcomes can be negative.

2. because the numerator is always less than or equal to the denominator

3. Answers may vary. Sample answer: A probability between 0.0 and 0.25 is a very low probability. A probability between 0.25 and 0.5 is a low probability. A probability between 0.5 and 0.75 is a probability that is better than 50-50 but not close to certainty. A probability between 0.75 and 1.0 is a probability that is considerably better than 50-50.

4. $\frac{2}{13}$; very poor probability of success

5. $\frac{4}{13}$, about 0.31; not a very good probability of success, definitely less than 50-50

6. $\frac{7}{13}$, about 0.54; the probability of success is better than 50-50, but still not very good.

7. $\frac{11}{13}$, about 0.85; very high probability of success

8. 0; she cannot guess a correct solution from the choices possible.

9. 1; any guess she makes is correct; the probability of success is as high as it can get.

10. Answers may vary. Sample answer: $2n - 6 \geq -5$

Lesson 4.4

1. 3   2. 73   3. 11   4. 39   5. 6.5

6. 6.5   7. 6.5   8. 8.5   9. 8.5   10. 8.5

11. The mean and median of a data set consisting of consecutive integers is equal to the average or mean of the first and last terms.

12. mean = median = 64

ANSWERS

13. mean = median = -5

14. mean = median = 10

15. mean = median = -4.5

16. a. mean = median = 15
   b. Yes; the numbers above and below the median increase or decrease by the same amount. Therefore, the median and the mean are the same.

17. The mean and median are given by $a + 1.5(k - 1)$.

Lesson 4.5

1. 25 students

2. newspaper delivery; 15 students

3. 65 students

4. convenience store   **5.** 45 students

6.

Raul's scores	
Each ○ represents 2 points	
Game 1	○○○○○○○
Game 2	○○○○○○○○○○◐
Game 3	○○○○○○○◐
Game 4	○○○○○○
Game 5	○○
Game 6	○○○○○○○○○◐
Game 7	○○○○○○○○○○○○

Lesson 4.6

1. mean: 7; median: 7.5; mode: 8

2. mean: about 7.17; median: 7.5; mode: 8

3. No, since the measures of comparable central tendencies are the same.

4.

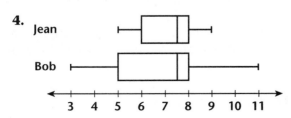

5. Jean's box plot is smaller than Bob's.

6. The whiskers in Bob's box plot are spread out much further than Jean's.

7. The spread of Bob's box plot is greater than Jean's and the lower quartile is less.

8. A box-and-whisker plot takes the spread of the data into account.

9. 3, 6, 7, 8, 9, 9, 10

10. Answers will vary but should include that a box-and-whisker plot does not give individual data values.

Enrichment—Chapter 5

Lesson 5.1

1. multiples of 5: . . . , $-15, -10, -5, 0, 5, 10, 15, . . .$

2. multiples of k: kn, where n is a variable integer and k is a fixed integer.

3. 0, 1, 2, 3, 4, 5, 6, 7, 8, 9 . . .

4. If P has coordinate a, Q has coordinate b, and P is to the left of Q, assign $a + \dfrac{a + b}{2}$.

5. If P has coordinate a, assign $|a|$.

6. If P has coordinate a and Q has coordinate b, assign $|a - b|$.

7. a. If the length of a side of the given square, X, is s, then $P(\text{square } X) = 4s$.
   b. If the length of a side of the given square X is s, then $A(\text{square } X) = s^2$.

8. a. The function rotates square A 120° counterclockwise about point O.
   b. The range is the set of all squares in the same plane. An individual square in the range is the same size as the original square.

ANSWERS

9. a.

(1, 1)	(1, 2)	(1, 3)	(1, 4)	(1, 5)	(1, 6)
(2, 1)	(2, 2)	(2, 3)	(2, 4)	(2, 5)	(2, 6)
(3, 1)	(3, 2)	(3, 3)	(3, 4)	(3, 5)	(3, 6)
(4, 1)	(4, 2)	(4, 3)	(4, 4)	(4, 5)	(4, 6)
(5, 1)	(5, 2)	(5, 3)	(5, 4)	(5, 5)	(5, 6)
(6, 1)	(6, 2)	(6, 3)	(6, 4)	(6, 5)	(6, 6)

b. {2, 3, 4, 5, 6, 7, 8, 9, 10, 11, 12}

Lesson 5.2

1.

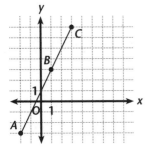

2. slope of $\overline{AB}$ = slope of $\overline{BC}$ = 2

3.

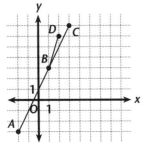

4. slope of $\overline{AB}$ = 2; slope of $\overline{BD}$ = 3

5. Points A, B, and C lie on the same line if the slopes of $\overline{AB}$, $\overline{BC}$, and $\overline{AC}$ are equal.

6. 3%   **7.** 300 feet

8. a. 6%
   b. They would report a different grade because the uphill grade is positive and the downhill grade is negative.

9. $2

Lesson 5.3

1. a. $y = 5t$, 40 minutes
   b. $y = 10t$, 20 minutes
   c. $y = 15t$, $13\frac{1}{3}$ minutes

2. a. $y = 15t$ **b.** $y = 25t$ **c.** $y = 30t$

3. a. $Q = 500 + 30t - 35t$
   b. emptying at 5 gallons per minute
   c. after 100 minutes, the tank will be empty

4. a. $Q = 500 + 30(t + 6) - 35t$,
      or $Q = 680 - 5t$
   b. after 136 minutes, the tank will be empty

Lesson 5.4

1. a. (6, 4)   **b.** (3, 6)   **c.** (0, 8)

2. (12, 0)   **3.** (0, 2)   **4.** (−3, 0)

5.

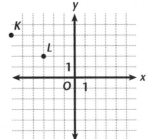

6. (0, 0)   **7.** (0, 0)

8. (−8, −10)

Lesson 5.5

1. Answers may vary. Sample answers:
   (6, −4) and (9, −8)

2. a.
$$4x + 3y = 12$$
$$-4x + 4x + 3y = -4x + 12$$
$$3y = -4x + 12$$
$$y = \frac{-4x}{3} + 4$$

   b. Answers may vary. Sample answers:
      (12, −12) and (15, −16)
   c. If x is a multiple of 3, y is a multiple of 4 and is an integer. If x is not a multiple of 3, y is not an integer.

ANSWERS

3. **a.** Check students' work
   b. -2 plus any multiple of 5; $-2 + 5x$

4. Choose x so that $-3x + 20$ is a multiple of 7, that is, -5 plus any multiple of 7

Lesson 5.6

1. **a.** $y = 2x + 4$
   b.

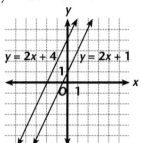

2. **a.** $(-2, -3)$ **b.** $y = -\frac{1}{2}x - 4$
   c.

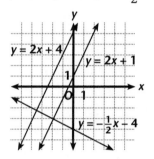

3. **a.** $(1, 3)$ **b.** $y = -\frac{1}{2}x + \frac{7}{2}$
   c.

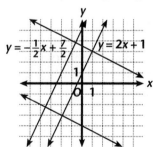

4. It is a parallelogram because opposite sides are parallel, and it is a rectangle because it has four right angles.

5. $x - y = -4$
   $x + y = 4$
   $x - y = 4$
   $x + y = -4$

6.

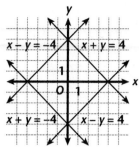

Enrichment—Chapter 6

Lesson 6.1

1. $0 < P \le 200$

2. No; because $2(70 + 40) = 220$ feet is greater than 200 feet

3. **a.** 80 feet **b.** 80 feet
   c. 1600 square feet

4. **a.** 60 feet **b.** 60 feet
   c. 2400 square feet

5. If the dimensions are reversed, the area remains the same.

6. **a.** 50 feet by 50 feet **b.** a square
   c. 2500 square feet

7. 40 feet by 40 feet

Lesson 6.2

1.

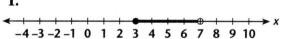

2. 3, 4, 5, 6

3. $x \ge 3$ and $x \le 6$ where x is an integer.

4. **a.** $x > 55$ **b.** $x > 0$ and $x < 40$

5. No, since there is a lower limit as well as an upper limit

6. **a.** $x \ge 40$ and $x \le 55$
   b. $x > 0$ and $x < 40$ or $x > 55$

ANSWERS

7. **a.** maximum: $190,000
   minimum: $180,000
   b. $x \geq \$180,000$ and $x \leq \$190,000$

8. $x \geq \$75,000$ and $x \leq \$255,000$

Lesson 6.3

1–6.

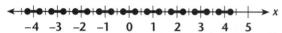

7. Answers may vary. Sample answer: closed intervals centered at each integer with each interval being 1 unit long

8. $n \leq x \leq n + \dfrac{1}{2}$

9. $2n \leq x \leq 2n + 1$

10. $4n - 1 \leq x \leq 4n + 1$

11. Answers may vary. Sample answers:
    a. The center of the interval is 1, and its length is $\dfrac{2}{n}$.
    b. As n gets larger, the center remains at 1, but the length of the interval gets smaller.

Lesson 6.4

1. **a.**
   ![number line from -4 to 4 with points at -2 and 2]
   b. 5
   c. 5; 5; The answers are the same.

2. **a.** ![number line from -4 to 4 with points at 1 and 3]
   b. 2
   c. 2; 2; The answers are the same.

3. **a.** ![number line from -4 to 4 with points at -2 and -1]
   b. 1
   c. 1; 1; The answers are the same.

4. Answers may vary. Sample answer: $|x - 2|$ is the distance between x and 2.

5. **a.**

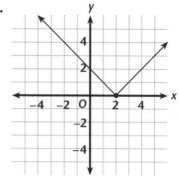

   b. $(2, 0)$
   c. Answers may vary. Sample answer: When $x = 2$, $|x - 2|$ is the distance between 2 and itself, or 0. Thus, $(2, 0)$ is included in the graph as the tip of the V.

6. Answers may vary. Sample answer: Either $|x + 3|$ or $|x - (-3)|$ is the distance between x and 3.

7. **a.**

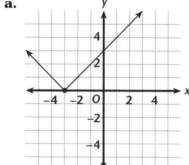

   b. $(-3, 0)$
   c. Answers may vary. Sample answer: When $x = -3$, $|x + 3|$ is the distance between -3 and itself, or 0. Thus, $(-3, 0)$ is included in the graph as the tip of the V.

Lesson 6.5

1. $x \geq 11.5$ and $x \leq 12.5$

2. $y \geq 8.5$ and $y \leq 9.5$

3. 11.5 feet by 8.5 feet

4. 12.5 feet by 9.5 feet

5. **a.** 40 feet   **b.** 44 feet
   c. 97.75 square feet
   d. 118.75 square feet

ANSWERS

6. a. 4 feet   **b.** 21 square feet

7. 928.625 cubic feet   **8.** 1246.875 cubic feet

9. 318.25 cubic feet

Enrichment—Chapter 7

Lesson 7.1

1.

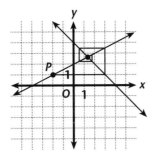

2.

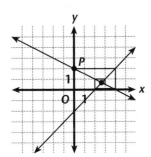

3.

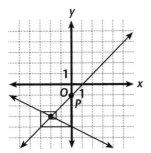

4. Each vertical line segment and each horizontal line segment gets longer than the previous vertical or horizontal line segment, respectively.

5. Line segments spiral away when:
a) the first line segment connecting the line with a smaller slope to the line with a larger slope (in absolute value terms) is a vertical line, or

b) the first line segment connecting the line with a larger slope to the line with the smaller slope (in absolute value terms) is a horizontal line.

Lesson 7.2

1. a. $4x = 7 - 3y$
   b. $7 - 3y + 4y = 12$
   c. $y = 5, x = -2$

2. a. $3(5 - 4y) - 2y + 3 = 0$
   $y = 1\frac{2}{7}$
   b. $\left(-\frac{1}{14}, 1\frac{2}{7}\right)$

3. a. $\begin{cases} 6x - 2y + 3 = 0 \\ 2x + 2(2y) - 5 = 0 \end{cases}$
   b. $2x + 2(6x + 3) - 5 = 0$
   $\left(-\frac{1}{14}, 1\frac{2}{7}\right)$

4. $\left(\frac{1}{4}, \frac{2}{3}\right)$ **5.** $(-2, 1)$ **6.** $\left(1\frac{1}{10}, \frac{47}{10k}\right)$

7. $\left(\frac{6}{17k}, 2\frac{15}{17}\right)$

8. Solve one of the equations for the common x-term and then substitute the equivalent expression for the common multiple in the other equation.

Lesson 7.3

1. $\begin{cases} 5x + 2y = -8 \\ 4x + 3y = 2 \end{cases}$

2. a. $\begin{cases} adx + bdy = de \\ -bcx - bdy = -bf \end{cases}$
   b. $adx - bcx = de - bf$
   $x = \dfrac{de - bf}{ad - bc}$
   c. $\begin{cases} acx + bcy = ce \\ -acx - ady = -af \end{cases}$
   d. $bcy - ady = ce - af$
   $y = \dfrac{ce - af}{bc - ad}$

3. $\left(1\frac{20}{29}, -1\frac{17}{29}\right)$ **4.** $\left(-5\frac{2}{7}, 5\frac{5}{7}\right)$

5. $(17, 11)$ **6.** $\left(\dfrac{sa}{r^2 + s^2}, \dfrac{ra}{r^2 + s^2}\right)$

7. The lines are parallel.

ANSWERS

Lesson 7.4

1. $\begin{cases} y = -\frac{1}{2}x + 8\frac{1}{2} \\ y = \frac{4}{9}x + 1\frac{8}{9} \\ y = \frac{7}{3}x + 5\frac{2}{3} \end{cases}$

2. $\begin{cases} y = \frac{4}{9}x + 1\frac{8}{9} \\ y = \frac{7}{3}x + 5\frac{2}{3} \end{cases}$

$\begin{cases} y = -\frac{1}{2}x + 8\frac{1}{2} \\ y = \frac{7}{3}x + 5\frac{2}{3} \end{cases}$

$\begin{cases} y = -\frac{1}{2}x + 8\frac{1}{2} \\ y = \frac{4}{9}x + 1\frac{8}{9} \end{cases}$

The vertices of the triangle are $(-2, 1)$, $(1, 8)$, and $(7, 5)$.

3. $\begin{cases} y = \frac{7}{3}x - 4 \\ y = -\frac{7}{3}x - 4 \\ y = \frac{1}{3}x + 4 \\ y = -\frac{1}{3}x + 4 \end{cases}$

4. $\begin{cases} y = -\frac{1}{3}x + 4 \\ y = -8x + 27 \\ y = -\frac{1}{3}x - 3\frac{2}{3} \\ y = -8x - 19 \end{cases}$

5. $\begin{cases} y = -\frac{4}{3}x + 4 \\ y = -\frac{4}{3}x - 3 \\ y = x + 4 \\ y = x - 3 \end{cases}$

6. a. $\begin{cases} y = \frac{1}{3}x + 4 \\ y = -\frac{1}{3}x + 4 \\ y = \frac{8}{3}x - 5 \\ y = -\frac{8}{3}x - 5 \end{cases}$

b. $\begin{cases} y = \frac{1}{3}x + 4 \\ y = -\frac{1}{3}x + 4 \\ y = \frac{8}{3}x - 5 \\ y = -\frac{8}{3}x - 5 \end{cases}$

Lesson 7.5

1. a–b.

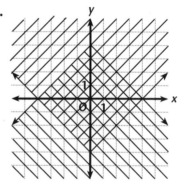

2. The solution is the interior of the parallelogram formed by the absolute value inequalities, including the boundary.

3.

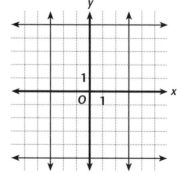

a. $|x| \le 3$
   $|y| \le 5$
b. $|x| \ge 3$
   $|y| \ge 5$

ANSWERS

----

4. Explanations may vary but should give the following absolute value inequalities: $|x - 1| \leq 2$ and $|y - 3| \leq 5$

5. $|x| \leq a$, where $a > 0$
$|y| \leq a$

Lesson 7.6

1. 72 and 27   **2.** 72 and 27   **3.** 72 and 27

4. Answers may vary.

5. a. $t + u = 4$, where t represents the tens digit and u represents the units digit.

b. Answers may vary. Sample answer: When the digits are reversed, one number is 8 less than three times the other number.

c. Answers may vary. Sample answer: When the digits are reversed, one number is 34 less than five times the other number.

Enrichment—Chapter 8

Lesson 8.1

		x^1	x^2	x^3	x^4	x^5	x^6	x^7	x^8	x^9
1.	$x = 1$	1	1	1	1	1	1	1	1	1
2.	$x = 2$	2	4	8	6	2	4	8	6	2
3.	$x = 3$	3	9	7	1	3	9	7	1	3
4.	$x = 4$	4	6	4	6	4	6	4	6	4
5.	$x = 5$	5	5	5	5	5	5	5	5	5
6.	$x = 6$	6	6	6	6	6	6	6	6	6
7.	$x = 7$	7	9	3	1	7	9	3	1	7
8.	$x = 8$	8	4	2	6	8	4	2	6	8
9.	$x = 9$	9	1	9	1	9	1	9	1	9
10.	$x = 10$	0	0	0	0	0	0	0	0	0

11. For all n, 1^n has 1 as its units digit.

12. The units digits follow the pattern 2, 4, 8, and 6, for $n = 1, 2, 3,$ and 4 and then repeat.

13. The units digits follow the pattern 3, 9, 7, and 1, for $n = 1, 2, 3,$ and 4 and then repeat.

14. For all $n > 0$, 5^n has 5 as its units digit.

15. If you divide n by 4, then the units digit is 7, 9, 3, or 1, depending on whether the remainder is 1, 2, 3, or 0, respectively.

Lesson 8.2

1.

n	$x = (-2)^n$	$y = (-2)^{n-1}$	(x, y)
1	-2	1	$(-2, 1)$
2	4	-2	$(4, -2)$
3	-8	4	$(-8, 4)$
4	16	-8	$(16, -8)$
5	-32	16	$(-32, 16)$
6	64	-32	$(64, -32)$
7	-128	64	$(-128, 64)$

2.

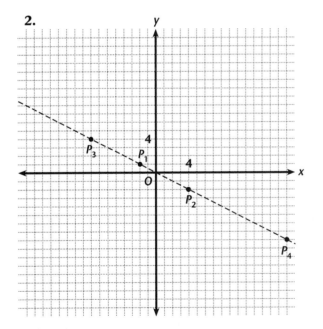

3. slope of $\overline{P_1P_2}$: $-\dfrac{1}{2}$; slope of $\overline{P_2P_3}$: $-\dfrac{1}{2}$;

slope of $\overline{P_1P_3}$: $-\dfrac{1}{2}$

ANSWERS

----

4. All the points lie along the line $y = -\frac{1}{2}x$.

When n increases from 1, the points alternate from the second quadrant to the fourth quadrant and vice versa. The points move farther away from the origin.

5. All the points lie along the line $y = x - 2$ and lie in the first quadrant. The points move farther away from the origin.

6. All the points lie along the line $y = -\frac{1}{3}x$.

When n increases from 1, the points alternate from the second quadrant to the fourth quadrant and vice versa. The points move farther away from the origin.

7. All the points lie along the line $y = \frac{1}{3}x$ and lie in the first quadrant. The points move farther away from the origin.

8. This set of points consists of the second, fourth, sixth, and so on points in the pattern of points in Exercise 1. All the points lie along the line $y = -\frac{1}{2}x$. When n increases from 1 on, the points alternate from being in the second quadrant to the fourth quadrant and vice versa. The points move farther away from the origin.

Lesson 8.3

1. 0.00012   **2.** 0.00048   **3.** 0.00009

4. 0.0000108   **5.** 0.00012   **6.** 0.00048

7. 0.00009   **8.** 0.0000108   **9.** 0.00000036

10. 0.000006

11. Multiply the decimals in the same way as the whole numbers. Count the number of decimal places in each of the three numbers. Find the sum of those numbers. Move the decimal point that many places to the left, starting at the right of the units digit in the product of whole numbers just calculated.

Lesson 8.4

1. $2^3 \times 3^1$ **2.** $2^2 \times 3^3$ **3.** $2^2 \times 113^1$

4. $2^3 \times 3^2 \times 5^2$ **5.** $\frac{3^1}{2^2}$ **6.** $\frac{2^2}{3^1 5^1}$ **7.** $\frac{5^3}{2^4 3^2}$

8. $\frac{3^1}{2^1 5^1}$

9. If b is prime, $\frac{b^n}{b^m}$ appears in the rational number, and $n > m$, then b will appear only in the numerator when the simplification is done. If b is prime, $\frac{b^n}{b^m}$ appears in the rational number, and $n < m$, then b will appear only in the denominator when the simplification is done. If b is prime, $\frac{b^n}{b^m}$ appears in the rational number, and $n = m$, then b will disappear from the numerator and the denominator when the simplification is done.

10. Every rational number can be written as a quotient whose numerator is 1 or the product of prime numbers raised to positive integer exponents and whose denominator can be written as 1 or the product of prime numbers raised to positive integer exponents, and there are no prime bases common to the numerator and the denominator.

Lesson 8.5

1. a. 9.3×10^7 miles
   b. 4.84×10^8 miles
   c. $\frac{4.84 \times 10^8}{9.3 \times 10^7}$; Jupiter is about 5.2 times as far from the sun as Earth is.

2. a. Pluto is about 39.5 times as far from the sun as Earth is.
   b. Pluto is about 7.6 times as far from the sun as Jupiter is.

3. The star closest to the sun is about 269,000 times as far from the sun as Earth is.

4. 5.9×10^{12}

5. a. about 1.17×10^{18}
   b. The nearest galaxy is about 1.3×10^{10} times as far from the sun as Earth is.

ANSWERS

- -

6. $\dfrac{6.35 \times 10^4}{1.67 \times 10^{-24}}$; about 3.8×10^{28} to 1

7. $\dfrac{5.97 \times 10^{24}}{1.67 \times 10^{-24}}$; about 3.6×10^{48} to 1

Lesson 8.6

1. The bases are reciprocals of each other. The graphs are reflections of one another across the y-axis.

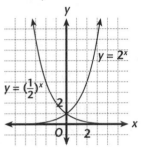

2. The bases are reciprocals of each other. The graphs are reflections of one another across the y-axis.

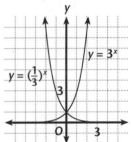

3. The bases are reciprocals of one another and the graphs are reflections of one another across the y-axis.

4. Because 10 and $\dfrac{1}{10}$ are reciprocals of one another, the graphs are reflections of one another across the y-axis.

5. Because $0.2 = \left(\dfrac{1}{5}\right)^x$ and 5 and $\dfrac{1}{5}$ are reciprocals of one another, the graphs are reflections of one another across the y-axis.

6. Because $4^{-x} = \left(\dfrac{1}{4}\right)^x$ and 4 and $\dfrac{1}{4}$ are reciprocals of one another, the graphs are reflections of one another across the y-axis.

7. Because $1.25^{-x} = \left(\dfrac{5}{4}\right)^{-x} = \left(\dfrac{4}{5}\right)^x$ and $\dfrac{5}{4}$ and $\dfrac{4}{5}$ are reciprocals of one another, the graphs are reflections of one another across the y-axis.

Lesson 8.7

1. $A = 10,000(1.0565)^t$

2.

t	0	1	2	3
A	10,000	10,565	11,161.92	11,792.57

t	4	5	6	7
A	12,458.85	13,162.78	13,906.47	14,692.19

3. a. sometime after the end of the third year but before the end of the fourth year
   b. sometime after the end of the third year but before the end of the fourth year and sometime after the end of the sixth year but before the end of the seventh year

4. after about 7.4 years

5. a. No; after 10 years, they will have $17,325.87, which is less than $18,000.
   b. They will fall short by about $674.13.

6. after about 8.3 years

7. after about 4.1 years

8. after about 153 years

9. after about 1065 years

Enrichment—Chapter 9

Lesson 9.1

1. $5 \times 10 + 6$
      $+ 3 \times 10 + 7$

$(5 + 3) \times 10 + 13 = (5 + 3) \times 10 + 1 \times 10 + 3$
$ = (5 + 3 + 1) \times 10 + 3$
$ = 9 \times 10 + 3$
$ = 93$

ANSWERS

2. $6 \times 10 + 7$

$\underline{+\ 1 \times 10 + 5}$

$(6 + 1) \times 10 + 12 = (6 + 1) \times 10 + 1 \times 10 + 2$

$= (6 + 1 + 1) \times 10 + 2$

$= 8 \times 10 + 2$

$= 82$

3. a. when the sum is 9 or less

   b. when the sum is 10 or more

4. No, the units digits of both numbers are never greater than 9, whose sum is 18.

5.

$7 \times 10 + 8$

$\underline{+\ 6 \times 10 + 7}$

$(7 + 6) \times 10 + 15$

$= (7 + 6) \times 10 + 1 \times 10 + 5$

$= (7 + 6 + 1) \times 10 + 5$

$= 14 \times 10 + 5$

$= (10 + 4) \times 10 + 5$

$= 1 \times 100 + 4 \times 10 + 5$

$= 145$

6.

$8 \times 10 + 7$

$\underline{+\ 7 \times 10 + 9}$

$(8 + 7) \times 10 + 16 = (8 + 7) \times 10 + 1 \times 10 + 6$

$= (8 + 7 + 1) \times 10 + 6$

$= 16 \times 10 + 6$

$= (10 + 6) \times 10 + 6$

$= 1 \times 100 + 6 \times 10 + 6$

$= 166$

7. Answers may vary. Sample answers:

$555 + 445$

$= 9 \times 100 + 9 \times 10 + 1 \times 10$

$= 9 \times 100 + (9 + 1) \times 10$

$= 9 \times 100 + 10 \times 10$

$= 9 \times 100 + 1 \times 100$

$= 10 \times 100$

$= 1000$

Lesson 9.2

	$(a + b)^2$	$(a - b)^2$	$(a + b)^2 - (a - b)^2$	ab
1.	4	64	−60	−15
2.	36	4	32	8
3.	81	9	72	18
4.	121	9	112	28
5.	9	169	−160	−40

6. a. The difference $(a + b)^2 - (a - b)^2$ is four times the product ab.

   b. $(a + b)^2 - (a - b)^2 = 4ab$

   c. $(a + b)^2 = a^2 + 2ab + b^2$

$(a - b)^2 = a^2 - 2ab + b^2$

$a^2 + 2ab + b^2 - (a^2 - 2ab + b^2) = 4ab$

Thus, $(a + b)^2 - (a - b)^2 = 4ab$

7. $(a + b)^2 + (a - b)^2 = 2a^2 + 2b^2$

8. $4a^4$ **9.** $4b^4$

10. $\left[(a^2 + b^2) + (a^2 - b^2)\right]^2$

$(a^2 + a^2 + b^2 - b^2)^2 = (2a^2)^2 = 2^2a^4 = 4a^4$

11. $\left[(a^2 + b^2) - (a^2 - b^2)\right]^2$

$(a^2 - a^2 + b^2 + b^2)^2 = (2b^2)^2 = 2^2b^4 = 4b^4$

Lesson 9.3

1.

$1 \times 10 + 3$

$\underline{\times\ 2 \times 10 + 2}$

$2 \times 10 + 6$

$\underline{+\ 2 \times 10 \times 10 + 6 \times 10}$

$2 \times 100 \qquad + 8 \times 10 + 6$

The product is 286.

2.

$1 \times 10 + 3$

$\underline{\times\ 1 \times 10 + 6}$

$(6 + 1) \times 10 + 8$

$\underline{+\ 1 \times 100 + 3) \times 10}$

$1 \times 100 + (6 + 1 + 3) \times 10 + 8$

$1 \times 100 + 10 \times 10 \qquad\qquad + 8$

$\underline{1 \times 100 + 1 \times 100 \qquad\qquad + 8}$

$2 \times 100 \qquad\qquad\qquad\qquad + 8$

The product is 208.

3. $(10t + 1)(10r + 1) = 100rt + 10(r + t) + 1$; If $rt \geq 10$, the product will be greater than 1000. If $r + t \geq 10$ and $rt \geq 9$, the product will be greater than 1000.

ANSWERS

Lesson 9.4

1.

x	y
−3	9
−2	4
−1	1
0	0
1	1
2	4
3	9

2.

x	y
−3	81
−2	16
−1	1
0	0
1	1
2	16
3	81

3.

x	y
−3	−27
−2	−8
−1	−1
0	0
1	1
2	8
3	27

4.

x	y
−3	−243
−2	−32
−1	−1
0	0
1	1
2	32
3	243

5. Each graph is U-shaped in the first and second quadrants opening upward and extending indefinitely. The origin is at the bottom of the U.

6. Each graph is S-shaped in the first and third quadrants extending indefinitely down to the left and up to the right. The origin is at the point on the graph where it moves from the third quadrant to the first quadrant.

7. Let $y = x^n$, where n is even and is 2 or more. Because $(-x)^n = x^n$, for a given x-value, the y-values are equal and positive for x and $-x$. Also $(0, 0)$ is on the graph. The graph is symmetric about the y-axis. Let $y = x^n$, where n is odd and is 3 or more. Because $(-x)^n = -x^n$, for a given x-value, the y-values are opposite one another for x and $-x$. Also $(0, 0)$ is on the graph. Thus the graph sweeps through the third quadrant, passes through the origin, and then sweeps through the first quadrant in an S shape.

Lesson 9.5

1. $3^1 5^2 11^1$ **2.** $3^2 5^2 7^1$ **3.** 2^{10} **4.** $2^4 3^2 5^2 7^1$

5. 2, 3, 5, and 7   **6.** 2 and 11

7. relatively prime   **8.** 3, 5, 17, and 31

9. $2^1 3^2 5^2 7^2$ **10.** $2^1 11^2$ **11.** 1

12. $3^2 5^5 17^2 31^5$ **13.** $2^3 3^4 7^1$ **14.** 1

Lesson 9.6

1.
$$\begin{array}{r} a^2 + ab + b^2 \\ \times \quad\quad a - b \\ \hline -ba^2 - ab^2 - b^3 \\ + a^3 + ba^2 + ab^2 \quad\quad \\ \hline a^3 \quad\quad\quad\quad - b^3 \end{array}$$

2. $a^4 - b^4 = (a^2)^2 - (b^2)^2$
$\qquad\qquad = (a^2 + b^2)(a^2 - b^2)$
$\qquad\qquad = (a^2 + b^2)(a + b)(a - b)$

ANSWERS

3.

$$\begin{array}{r} a^2 - ab + b^2 \\ \times \qquad a + b \\ \hline ba^2 - ab^2 + b^3 \\ + a^3 - ba^2 + ab^2 \qquad \\ \hline a^3 \qquad\qquad + b^3 \end{array}$$

4 a. If two polynomials are equal, their corresponding coefficients are equal. The coefficients of a^2, ab, and b^2 are equal.

b. If $t = 0$ and $u = 0$, then r and s are given by undefined expressions. Thus, there are no numbers r, s, t, and u for which $a^2 + b^2$ can be factored as $(ra + sb)(ta + bu)$.

Lesson 9.7

1. Distributive Property

2. $\left(\dfrac{1}{2}\right)\left(\dfrac{1}{3}\right) = \dfrac{1 \times 1}{2 \times 3} = \dfrac{1}{6}$

$\dfrac{1}{2} + \dfrac{1}{3} = \dfrac{1}{2} \times \dfrac{3}{3} + \dfrac{1}{3} \times \dfrac{2}{2} = \dfrac{3 + 2}{2 \times 3} = \dfrac{5}{6}$

3. $6\left(x + \dfrac{1}{2}\right)\left(x + \dfrac{1}{3}\right) = 2\left(x + \dfrac{1}{2}\right) \times 3\left(x + \dfrac{1}{3}\right)$

$\qquad\qquad = (2x + 1)(3x + 1)$
$\qquad\qquad = 6x^2 + 3x + 2x + 1$
$\qquad\qquad = 6x^2 + 5x + 1$

4. Yes; the given polynomial expression is written as a product of polynomials of lower degree. There is no requirement that the coefficients be integers.

5. $15\left(x + \dfrac{1}{5}\right)\left(x + \dfrac{1}{3}\right)$ **6.** $28\left(x + \dfrac{1}{7}\right)\left(x + \dfrac{1}{4}\right)$

7. $6\left(x - \dfrac{4}{3}\right)\left(x - \dfrac{5}{2}\right)$ **8.** $12\left(x - \dfrac{5}{3}\right)\left(x + \dfrac{7}{4}\right)$

9. Suppose that $x^2 + x + 1 = \left(x + \dfrac{p}{q}\right)\left(x + \dfrac{r}{s}\right)$, where p, q, r, and s are integers.

Thus, $\left(\dfrac{p}{q}\right)\left(\dfrac{r}{s}\right) = 1$ and $\dfrac{p}{q} + \dfrac{r}{s} = 1$.

Thus, $\dfrac{p}{q} + \dfrac{q}{p} = 1$. If $0 < \dfrac{p}{q} \le 1$, then

$\dfrac{p}{q} + \dfrac{q}{p} > 1$. If $-1 \le \dfrac{p}{q} < 0$, then

$\dfrac{p}{q} + \dfrac{q}{p} < -1$. There are no p and q so that

$\dfrac{p}{q} + \dfrac{q}{p} = 1$. Thus, $x^2 + x + 1$ does not factor as required.

Lesson 9.8

1. $(3x - 1)(2x + 1)$; $\dfrac{1}{3}$ and $-\dfrac{1}{2}$

2. $(5x + 2)(x - 3)$; $-\dfrac{2}{5}$ and 3

3. $(3x - 4)(2x - 5)$; $\dfrac{4}{3}$ and $\dfrac{5}{2}$

4. $(4x + 7)(3x - 5)$; $-\dfrac{7}{4}$ and $\dfrac{5}{3}$

5. s and u are factors of c.

6. Each numerator of a root are factors of c.

7. According to Exercise 3, $6x^2 - 23x + 20 = 0$ has $\dfrac{4}{3}$ and $-\dfrac{5}{2}$ as its roots. The numerators, 4 and 5, of the roots are factors of 20, the constant term. The denominators, 3 and 2, of the roots are factors of 6, the coefficient of x^2.

Enrichment — Chapter 10

Lesson 10.1

1.

x	-1	0	1	2	3	4	5
y	21	11	5	3	5	11	21

x	1.7	1.8	1.9	2.0	2.1	2.2	2.3
y	3.18	3.08	3.02	3.00	3.02	3.08	3.18

2. $(2, 3)$ **3.** $x = 2$ **4.** 2

5.

x	-1.3	-1.2	-1.1	-1.0	-0.9	-0.8	-0.7
y	-2.27	-2.12	-2.03	-2.00	-2.03	-2.12	-2.27

6. $(-1, -2)$ **7.** $x = -1$ **8.** -1

9. a. An equation for the axis of symmetry of the graph of $y = ax^2 + bx + c$ is $x = \dfrac{-b}{2a}$.

b. One approach is to use graphs, and a second approach is to use tables as in Exercises 1 and 5.

ANSWERS

Lesson 10.2

1. 3 and 4

2. **a.** 12.25
   b. $3.5 > \sqrt{12}$
   c. 3.5
   d. ≈ 3.428
   e. ≈ 3.464

3. up to 3 places, depending on how the numbers were rounded

4. ≈ 3.6 **5.** ≈ 4.5

6. No; the square root will be an irrational number which cannot be written as a terminating decimal.

Lesson 10.3

1. $y = \left(x + \dfrac{5}{2}\right)^2 - 1 - \dfrac{5^2}{4}$

2. $y = \left(x - \dfrac{11}{2}\right)^2 + 6 - \dfrac{11^2}{4}$

3. $y = \left(x + \dfrac{b}{2}\right)^2 + c - \dfrac{b^2}{4}$

4. $\left(\dfrac{-b}{2}, c - \dfrac{b^2}{4}\right)$

5. $a > 0$

6. If the parabola opens upward and the y-coordinate of the vertex is greater than 0, then the parabola is completely above the x-axis. If it is is less than 0, then the parabola crosses the x-axis at two points. If it is equal to 0, then the parabola touches the x-axis at one point.

7. **a.** 0   **b.** 1   **c.** 2

8. **a.** $(-1, -9)$ **b.** 2

9. **a.** $(4.5, -2.25)$ **b.** 2

Lesson 10.4

1. It crosses the x-axis.

2. $-1.41, -0.84, -0.25, 0.36, 0.99, 1.64, 2.31$

3. **a.** $x \geq 5.6$ **b.** $x \leq 5.5$

4. Between 5.5 and 5.6, the y-coordinate changes from negative to positive, so the graph crosses the x-axis which further confirms that the graph crosses the axis between 5 and 6.

5. yes   **6.** ≈ 5.54 **7.** ≈ -0.54

8. $33, 8, -5, -6, 5, 28, 63$
   There is a zero between -2 and -1, and there is another zero between 0 and 1.

Lesson 10.5

1. $a = 2; b = -5; c = -8$

2. $a = 7; b = 0; c = -56$

3. $a = 12; b = -16; c = 0$

4. $a = 0$; there is no $x^2 -$ term

5. 2   **6.** 3   **7.** 1

8. answers may vary

9. answers may vary

10. answers may vary

11. $x = 0$

12. $x = \pm\sqrt{\dfrac{c}{a}}$

13. $x = \dfrac{-b}{a}$ or $x = 0$

14. $x = \dfrac{-b \pm \sqrt{b^2 - 4ac}}{2a}$

15. the quadratic formula

ANSWERS

Lesson 10.6

1. parabola

2. Answers may vary. Sample answer: One parabola is wider than the other and has its vertex above the other vertex but on the same axis of symmetry.

3. $y \geq x^2$

4.
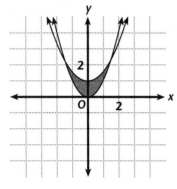

5. This shaded region is wider.

6. The "smile" disappears.

7. The "smile" widens as a gets closer to 1 in value.

8. This is not a "smile" anymore.

9. Answers may vary. Sample answer: $y \geq -0.25x^2 - 1$ and $y \leq -x^2$ will give a "frown."

Enrichment—Chapter 11

Lesson 11.1

1. $5\frac{1}{3}$ feet   2. $83\frac{1}{3}$ pounds

3. Box A is $6\frac{2}{3}$ feet from the pivot point; box B is $5\frac{1}{3}$ feet from the pivot point.

4. $11\frac{1}{4}$ feet

5. No; box B would have to be $11\frac{1}{4}$ feet from the pivot point. The board is not long enough.

6. **a.** $L = \frac{7}{4}x$ **b.** $x = \frac{4}{7}L$

Lesson 11.2

1.
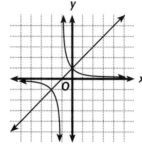

break at $x = -1$

2.
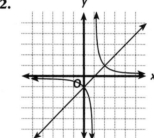

break at $x = 1$

3. $y = x - 2.5$ and $y = \dfrac{1}{x - 2.5}$

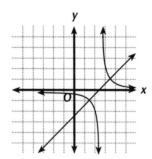

4. $y = x - 3$ and $y = \dfrac{1}{x - 3}$

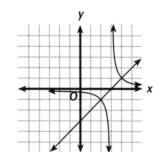

5. $y = x + 3$ and $y = \dfrac{1}{x + 3}$

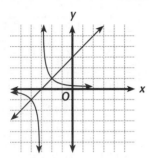

Lesson 11.3

1. a. $e = 2r$ **b.** $r = \dfrac{e}{2}$

2. $R = \dfrac{r}{3}$ **3.** $R = \dfrac{e}{6}$

4.

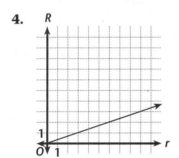

The volume of the sphere is $\dfrac{r}{3}$ times the surface area of the sphere.

5.

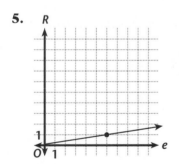

The volume of the cube is $\dfrac{e}{6}$ times the surface area of the cube.

6. The volume of the cube is $\dfrac{6}{\pi}$ times that of the sphere.

Lesson 11.4

1. Because $d = rt$, $t = \dfrac{d}{r}$.

2. 49.5 miles per hour

3. a. $\dfrac{2rs}{r + s}$ **b.** $\dfrac{2rs}{r + s} \neq \dfrac{1}{2}(r + s)$

4. 49.5 miles per hour

5. The rates for segment BC are exactly the same as those for segment AB.

Lesson 11.5

1. $x = 2, y = 2$

2. Answers may vary. Sample answer: $x = 4$, $y = 4$

3. Answers may vary. Sample answer: $x = 8$, $y = 8$

4. Answers may vary. Sample answer: $x = 12$, $y = 12$

5. Answers may vary. Sample answer: $x = 16$, $y = 16$

6. Answers may vary. Sample answer: $x = 200, y = 200$

7. $x = 2n, y = 2n$

8. a. $\dfrac{1}{1} + \dfrac{1}{1} = 2$

b. If x and y are integers with $0 < \dfrac{1}{x} < 1$ and $0 < \dfrac{1}{y} < 1$, then $0 < \dfrac{1}{x} + \dfrac{1}{y} < 2$. Therefore, $\dfrac{1}{x} + \dfrac{1}{y} = 2$ is only true when $x = 1$ and $y = 1$.

c. Since $0 < \dfrac{1}{x} + \dfrac{1}{y} < 2$, there are no positive integers x and y for $n > 2$.

9. Answers may vary. Sample answer: $x = 6, y = 6$

10. Answers may vary. Sample answer: $x = 10, y = 10$

Lesson 11.6

1. If $x < 0$, then multiplying both sides of $x \geq x - 1$ by x would give $x^2 \leq x^2 - x$ and $0 \geq x$.

2. In this problem $a - b = 0$, so division by $a - b$ is not permitted.

3. The first statement is incorrect; $\sqrt{r} \neq r$ unless $r = 0$ or $r = 1$.

4. The substitution is incorrect; $y = 2 - x$, which gives $x + (2 - x) = 6$, or $2 = 6$, which is false.

5. $\sqrt{a^2} = |a|$ and $\sqrt{b^2} = |b|$; this does not imply that $a = b$. For example, $|-3| = |3|$, but $-3 \neq 3$.

6. $\sqrt{2a^2} \neq 2a$; rather, $\sqrt{2a^2} = |a|\sqrt{2}$.

7. Mia will always be one year younger than Jon.

Enrichment—Chapter 12

Lesson 12.1

1. 6 **2.** $10\sqrt{2}$ **3.** -41 **4.** $\dfrac{59 + 30\sqrt{2}}{-41}$

5. $2a$ **6.** $2b\sqrt{2}$ **7.** $a^2 - 2b^2$

8. $\dfrac{a^2 + 2b^2 + 2ab\sqrt{2}}{a^2 - 2b^2}$

9. The product is the rational number $a^2 - nb^2$.

10. -87

11. The quotient is the numerator squared, $(a + b\sqrt{n})^2$ divided by $a^2 - b^2 n$.

12. $\dfrac{11 + 4\sqrt{7}}{-3}$

Lesson 12.2

1. Their graphs do not intersect.

2. Their graphs do not intersect.

3. Their graphs do not intersect.

4. $x - 2 \neq x - 4$ for all values of x

5. $x - 2 \neq x - 6$ for all values of x

6. $x - 4 \neq x - 6$ for all values of x

7.

x	10	20	50
$\sqrt{x}$	3.162	4.472	7.071
$\sqrt{x-2}$	2.828	4.243	6.928
$\sqrt{x} - \sqrt{x-2}$	0.334	0.229	0.143

x	100	200	500
$\sqrt{x}$	10	14.142	22.361
$\sqrt{x-2}$	9.899	14.071	22.316
$\sqrt{x} - \sqrt{x-2}$	0.101	0.071	0.045

x	1000	5000
$\sqrt{x}$	31.623	70.711
$\sqrt{x-2}$	31.591	70.697
$\sqrt{x} - \sqrt{x-2}$	0.032	0.014

8. In the expression $\sqrt{x} - \sqrt{x - n}$, as n remains constant and x becomes larger, the expression gets closer to 0 in value.

Lesson 12.3

1. a. $\dfrac{1}{2}(a + b)(a + b)$

   b. $\dfrac{1}{2}(a + b)^2$ or $\dfrac{1}{2}a^2 + ab + \dfrac{1}{2}b^2$

2. $\dfrac{1}{2}ab + \dfrac{1}{2}ab + \dfrac{1}{2}c^2$ or $ab + \dfrac{1}{2}c^2$

3. Since both answers are expressions for the area of the trapezoid
$$\dfrac{1}{2}a^2 + ab + \dfrac{1}{2}b^2 = ab + \dfrac{1}{2}c^2$$
$$\dfrac{1}{2}a^2 + \dfrac{1}{2}b^2 = \dfrac{1}{2}c^2$$
$$a^2 + b^2 = c^2$$

4. c^2

5. a. $a - b$ by $a - b$
   b. $(a - b)^2 = a^2 - 2ab + b^2$

6. $4\left(\dfrac{1}{2}ab\right) = 2ab$

7. The sum of the areas of the white square and the 4 triangles should be the area of the larger square, c^2.
$$4\left(\dfrac{1}{2}\right)ab + (a - b)^2 = c^2$$
$$2ab + a^2 - 2ab + b^2 = c^2$$
$$a^2 + b^2 = c^2$$

ANSWERS

Lesson 12.4

1. 7 **2.** 15 **3.** 8 **4.** 8

5. Michael; if the points are the endpoints of a horizontal or vertical segment, the Manhattan distance will be the same as the actual, or Pythagorean, distance.

6. The sum of two absolute values is always nonnegative.

7. $12; |6 - 1| + |9 - 2| = 12$

8. $20; |-5 - 5| + |5 - (-5)| = 20$

Lesson 12.5

1. $M_1(-1, 0); M_2(0, 4); M_3(4, -1)$

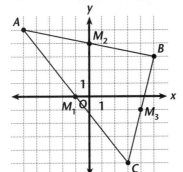

2. a.

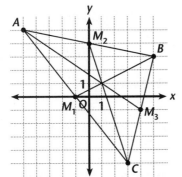

b. Yes; they appear to intersect at the point (1, 1).

3. $y = \frac{1}{2}x + \frac{1}{2}$ **4.** $y = -3x + 4$

5. $y = -\frac{2}{3}x + \frac{5}{3}$

6. $\begin{cases} y = \frac{1}{2}x + \frac{1}{2} \\ y = -3x + 4 \end{cases}$; (1, 1)

7. $\begin{cases} y = -3x + 4 \\ y = -\frac{2}{3}x + \frac{5}{3} \end{cases}$; (1, 1)

8. The point (1, 1) is on all three segments.

9.

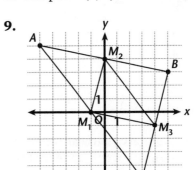

$\triangle M_1M_2M_3$ is similar to $\triangle ABC$. Each side of $\triangle M_1M_2M_3$ is parallel to and is $\frac{1}{2}$ as long as a side of $\triangle ABC$. The area of $\triangle M_1M_2M_3$ is $\frac{1}{4}$ the area of $\triangle ABC$.

Lesson 12.6

1. a.

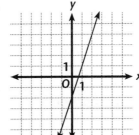

b. 3
c. $\tan\angle QPR = \frac{3}{1} = 3$

2. a.

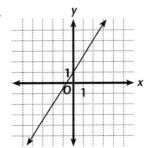

b. 1.5
c. $\tan\angle QPR = \frac{3}{2} = 1.5$

ANSWERS

3. a.

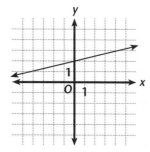

b. 0.25

c. $\tan\angle QPR = \dfrac{1}{4} = 0.25$

4. The slope of the graph of a linear equation is equal to the tangent of the angle that the line makes with the horizontal.

5. Find the acute angle which has a tangent equal to 2.4. $\tan^{-1} 2.4 \approx 67.4°$

Lesson 12.7

1. 222.1 feet   **2.** 549.5 feet

3. 298.9 feet   **4.** 584.8 feet

5. a. 327.4 feet

b. $AB = \dfrac{h}{\tan 20°} - \dfrac{h}{\tan 42°}$

6. 343.4 feet   **7.** 7369.1 yards

8. a. definition of tangent ratio applied twice
b. Solve the second equation for d_2. Substitute into the first equation. Apply the Distributive Property.
c. 977.5 yards

Lesson 12.8

1. a. $\begin{bmatrix} a+c & 0 \\ 0 & b+d \end{bmatrix}$

b. Yes; all elements not on the main diagonal are 0.

2. a. $\begin{bmatrix} ac & 0 \\ 0 & bd \end{bmatrix}$

b. Yes; all elements not on the main diagonal are 0.

3. The set is closed under both addition and multiplication because the results of both operations are 2×2 diagonal matrices.

4. a. $RT = TR = \begin{bmatrix} 1 & 0 \\ 0 & 1 \end{bmatrix}$

b. Matrix R acts like a reciprocal with respect to T, and T acts like a reciprocal with respect to R.

5. $a = \pm 1$ and $b = \pm 1$

6. sum: a diagonal matrix whose main diagonal elements are the sums of the diagonal elements in the matrices being added; product: a diagonal matrix whose main diagonal elements are the products of the diagonal elements in the matrices being multiplied

7. If $a \neq 0$, $b \neq 0$, and $c \neq 0$, then

$$N = \begin{bmatrix} \dfrac{1}{a} & 0 & 0 \\ 0 & \dfrac{1}{b} & 0 \\ 0 & 0 & \dfrac{1}{c} \end{bmatrix}.$$

Enrichment—Chapter 13

Lesson 13.1

1. {100, 250, 500, 1000, 5000}

2. $\dfrac{4}{16}$, or $\dfrac{1}{4}$ **3.** $\dfrac{3}{16}$ **4.** $\dfrac{2}{16}$, or $\dfrac{1}{8}$ **5.** $\dfrac{1}{16}$

6. $\left\{ \dfrac{1}{16}, \dfrac{1}{8}, \dfrac{3}{16}, \dfrac{1}{4}, \dfrac{3}{8} \right\}$ **7.** 1

8. The total of the probabilities for all possible events must be 1.

9. No; the range of functions can vary widely. A sum of 1 is only required for a probability function such as the one used here.

10. $\dfrac{9}{16}$ **11.** $\dfrac{5}{16}$ **12.** $\dfrac{3}{16}$ **13.** $\dfrac{6}{16}$, or $\dfrac{3}{8}$

14. $\dfrac{10}{16}$, or $\dfrac{5}{8}$ **15.** 0

ANSWERS

Lesson 13.2

1.

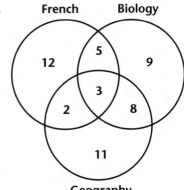

French   Biology

12   5   9

3

2   8

11

Geography

2. 50   **3.** $\frac{22}{50}$, or 0.44   **4.** $\frac{25}{50}$, or 0.5

5. $\frac{9}{50}$, or 0.18   **6.** $\frac{12}{50}$, or 0.24

7. $\frac{28}{50}$, or 0.56   **8.** $\frac{25}{50}$, or 0.5

9. $\frac{32}{50}$, or 0.64   **10.** $\frac{15}{50}$, or 0.3

Lesson 13.3

1.

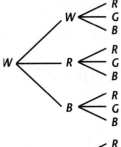

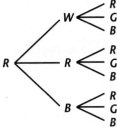

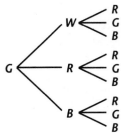

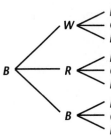

2. 36   **3.** 2   **4.** 34   **5.** 18   **6.** 24   **7.** 14

Lesson 13.4

1. $\frac{8}{24}$, or $\frac{1}{3}$ **2.** $\frac{7}{23}$ **3.** $\frac{56}{552}$, or $\frac{7}{69}$

4. $\frac{132}{552}$, or $\frac{11}{46}$ **5.** $\frac{6}{n}$ **6.** $\frac{5}{n-1}$ **7.** $\frac{30}{n(n-1)}$

8. $\frac{1}{n}$ **9.** $\frac{1}{n-1}$ **10.** $\frac{1}{n-2}$

11. $\frac{1}{n(n-1)(n-2)}$

12. Your chances of drawing a 1 get better until the 1 is drawn.

ANSWERS

Lesson 13.5

1. Answers may vary. Check students' work.

2. Answers may vary. Check students' work.

Enrichment—Chapter 14

Lesson 14.1

1. 104°F

2. Answers may vary. Sample answer: the 112°F may have been a "heat index" reading.

3. For each value of C there is exactly 1 value for F.

4. **a.** (25, 77)   **b.** (−10, 14)
   c. (18, 64.4)   **d.** (30, 86)

5. $C = \frac{5}{9}(F - 32)$

6. **a.** (15, 59)   **b.** (25, 77)
   c. (−20, −4)   **d.** (26.7, 80)

7. Yes; for each value of F, there is exactly one value of C.

8. The result is the original 35.

9. −40°C is equivalent to −40°F.

Lesson 14.2

1. translated 2 units to the right

2. a parabola with its vertex at $(n, 0)$ on the x-axis

3. part of a parabola with a closed endpoint on the left and an open endpoint on the right

4. 1, 0.25, 0, 0.25, 1, 2.25, 4, 6.25

5.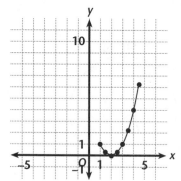

6.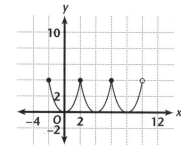

7. Answers may vary. Sample answer: The y-coordinates of points on the graph repeat at a regular interval of x-values.

Lesson 14.3

1.

x	−2	8	8	−2
y	−0.5	−0.5	1	1

2.

x	−2	3	6	1
y	−1	−1	2	2

3.

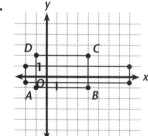

ANSWERS

4.

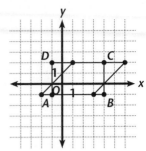

5. stretched horizontally by a factor of 2; stretched vertically by a factor of 0.5 (compressed)

6. parallelogram with the same measurements for height and base as those for the rectangle

7. Answers may vary; Sample answers:
  a. $(x, y) \rightarrow (x, 0.5y)$
  b. $(x, y) \rightarrow (2x, y)$

Lesson 14.4

1. The distances are equal.

2. ℓ is the perpendicular bisector of $\overline{A'A}$.

3. B' is in a direction perpendicular to line ℓ and the same distance from ℓ on the other side of ℓ.

4.

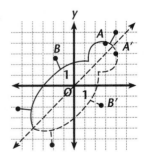

5.

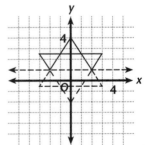

6. The coordinates for x and y are exchanged, that is $A(x, y)$ becomes $A'(y, x)$.

Lesson 14.5

1.

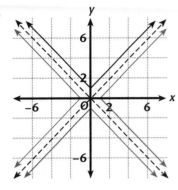

2.

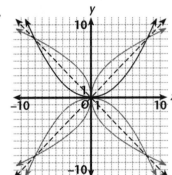

3.

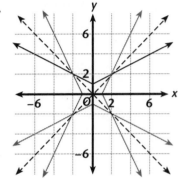

4.

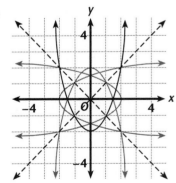

5. Answers may vary.